birth

● In the womb

When you were conceived you began to develop as a unique person in whom God is interested.

✳ Psalm 139:13-16

What did God do in your mother's womb (v 13)? _____

What else did he do (v 15)? _____

What was David's view of his own body (v 14)?

_____

Heartsearch

What is your view of your own body?

☐ it is wonderfully made by God

☐ it is not very nice   ☐ it is a problem

☐ it is an instrument for the service of God

☐ it is the temple of the Holy Spirit

What do you make of verse 16? _____

_____

✳ Job 10:8-12   Who gave Job his life? _____

✳ Jeremiah 1:5

When did God first know Jeremiah? _____

When did God set him apart? _____

What did God call him to do? _____

✳ Ephesians 1:4-5   ✳ 1 Peter 1:1-2

Has it ever occurred to you that God formed you in the womb for a purpose — he has called you to serve him and has a special job for you to do?

Do you know what God has called *you* to do?

Think!

✳ Luke 1:26-38

God himself chose to occupy a human body which was formed in the womb of Mary. This birth was unique in that there was no human father and the child was conceived by the Holy Spirit.

What was the call on Jesus's life?

_____

✳ Luke 1:39-45

What evidence is there of spiritual awareness in the foetus of John the Baptist?

_____

_____

How many months pregnant was Elizabeth

(v 26)? _____

● Birth

✳ Genesis 3:16

Why is there pain in childbearing?

_____

✳ Psalm 22:9-10, 71:5-6

When did your reliance on God begin? _____

● Welcoming babies

✳ Psalm 127:3-5

What are children? _____

In the Bible there was great rejoicing at the birth of children. They were a precious gift from God and a reward for serving him *(Psalm 128:1-6)* and there was every reason to celebrate and be thankful. Israelite boys were circumcised on the eighth day and named *(Luke 1:59-60, 2:21)*. There is no special ceremony described for babies of Christians in the New Testament but many parents like to dedicate their children to God and give opportunity for prayer and prophecy over them *(Luke 1:57-80)*. Jesus made a point of welcoming babies *(Luke 18:15-17)*.

Think!

Do you know of special prayers or prophecies over you when you were born?

What were they? _____

● Naming of babies

Names in the Bible were chosen carefully and emphasised the importance and uniqueness of the individual. God has a personal name ("Yahweh" - see *Exodus 3:13-14*). Names were chosen because of circumstances surrounding the birth, in thanks to God, as a prophetic statement, or at the command of God. What do the following names mean?

Isaac (Gen 18:10-15, 21:1-7) _____

Esau (Gen 25:25) _____

Jacob (Gen 25:26) _____

Samuel (1 Sam 1:20) _____

Jesus (Matt 1:21) _____

Do you know what *your* name means?

_____

Some other names
Isaiah - Yahweh saves
Ezekiel - God strengthens
Elijah - Yahweh is my God
John - Yahweh is gracious

Heartsearch

Memories!

What is your earliest memory?

_____

What is your earliest memory of your parent(s)?

_____

What is your earliest memory of spiritual awareness or anything to do with God?

_____

_____

● Born again - born of God

✳ **John 1:12-13, 3:1-16**   ✳ **1 Peter 1:3, 1:23**

How do you know if you are born again?

1 John 2:29, 3:9 _____   1 John 4:7 _____

1 John 5:1 _____   1 John 5:4 _____

birth

extra thought and discussion

• Spiritual state at birth

Human beings are different from the rest of creation. We are made in the image of God with a capacity for a wonderful relationship with God (Gen 1:26-27). Unfortunately, our original perfect state has been damaged by sin (Gen 3:1-24) and at birth we inherit the sinful nature and a tendency to sin (Gen 5:3, 8:21, Ps 51:5, Rom 5:12). It is not long before we sin ourselves (Ps 58:3, Rom 3:23). The Christian gospel is God's solution to this basic problem.

• Our existence

We did not exist in any form before our conception. We were created during the process from conception to birth. It is true that we were foreknown, chosen by God and even predestined from eternity in the past (1 Pet 1:2, Rom 8:28-30, Eph 1:5,11) but our actual existence extends from conception to eternity in the future (John 3:16).

We only have one life on this earth — not a series of lives with reincarnation (Heb 9:27).

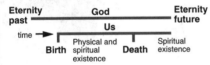

Jesus is the only human being who existed from eternity past as the Word of God. The Word became flesh as he developed in the womb and was born (John 1:1-14, 3:13, 8:58, 17:5).

• A living being?

Each person's unique genetic makeup is determined at the moment of conception.

The Bible teaches that God is involved in our development in the womb and there is evidence for spiritual awareness (see earlier in this unit).

The word soul is used to indicate our life, our being or our personality (Ezek 18:4). The word spirit (or breath or wind) is also used for the life which God gives us (Gen 2:7, 6:17, Ezek 37:7-10). The Bible has an integrated view of body, soul and spirit and so they are not distinguished clearly (Mark 12:30).

Spiritual life is complete when we are born again and have eternal life (John 3:1-16).

• Contraception

There is only one example of contraception in the Bible (Gen 38:8-10). In this episode Onan was obliged to sleep with his dead brother's wife to preserve the family line. He avoided his responsibility by withdrawal during intercourse. This method is not condemned, but his avoidance of his responsibility is.

In assessing contraception it is relevant to consider whether the method chosen prevents conception (eg condom or pills) or if it initiates a very early abortion after conception (eg coil or morning-after pill).

• Abortion

The fact that abortion is legal does not make it right. Many Christians are opposed to the practice of abortion for several reasons.

- It interferes with the creative activity of God in the womb.
- There is no regard for the rights of the individual in the womb. All have equal rights (Job 31:13-15).
- We have no right to take human life (Ex 20:13).
- Injury to pregnant women is condemned (Amos 1:13).
- There may be psychological damage to a mother who consents to abortion which may show itself in later life — guilt and shame.

• Miscarriage, still-birth, physical and mental abnormality, cot-death

This world is far from perfect. Babies die before, at or after birth, they are born deformed or with serious disabilities. The natural question to ask is "Why?".

The Biblical explanation of imperfection includes the general fallen state of creation caused by the activity of the devil and the sin of human beings. At the moment, nature is spoilt and we see imperfection, disease, death, decay and evil spread around the world, often unfairly, and we see human beings struggling (Gen 3:17-19).

It is significant that Jesus made a stand against this imperfection in his many miracles - on one occasion he healed a man who was born blind (John 9:1-7). Later his followers healed people who had been crippled from birth (Acts 3:1-10, 14:8-10).

Our creator God may still overrule and intervene by his power in response to the cries of his people today. Also we have made great strides medically to improve and preserve life. We look forward to a day when all evil will be destroyed (Rom 8:18-25, Rev 21:1-4, 22:1-5).

• Failure to conceive

Barrenness caused great distress and sadness in the Bible. Women felt that they had failed their husbands (1 Sam 1:1-16) and went to desperate ends to have children (Gen 16:1-4, Gen 30:1-6).

Childlessness was seen as the hand of God and occasionally as judgment by God. There were several cases of barren women eventually conceiving and we can be encouraged in persevering in prayer for those with this problem.

Bible examples — Sarah (Gen 21:1-7), Rachel (Gen 30:22-24), Samson's mother (Judg 13:1-25), Hannah (1 Sam 1:17-20), Elizabeth (Luke 1:5-7, 23-25).

childhood

● Jesus welcomed children

✳ Matthew 19:13-15

How did Jesus welcome children?

_____

Why should children come to Jesus?

_____

✳ Matthew 18:1-4

In what way do we all need to be like children?

_____

✳ Matthew 11:25-26   ✳ 1 Corinthians 1:26-29

What other factors enable children to be responsive to God?

_____

✳ Matthew 18:5-6

Why is it important for us to welcome children too?

_____

How would you describe the way you relate to and communicate with children?

☐ very good   ☐ good   ☐ poor   ☐ very poor

In what ways could adults cause children to sin?

_____

✳ Matthew 21:14-16

What else can we learn from children?

_____

5

● Children can be called by God to serve him

✳ 1 Samuel 3:1-21

What aspects of Samuel's character enabled him to hear God?

Here I am God !

_____

_____

God gave a heavy message to Samuel. Why do you think he chose a boy and not a responsible adult ?

_____

Children can become Christians at an early age and can be quite receptive to God. Their thinking can be less cluttered than adults'.

✳ John 6:9   How did this boy serve Jesus? _____

● Children should be trained and taught about God

✳ 2 Timothy 1:5   ✳ 2 Timothy 3:14-15

Who taught Timothy about God from an early age?

_____

✳ Proverbs 22:6

What is the effect of good training?

_____

✳ Deuteronomy 6:6-9

When should this training and teaching take place?

_____

✳ Deuteronomy 31:12-13   ✳ 2 Chronicles 20:13

How else can it happen?

_____

● Adults are an example

✳ 1 Kings 9:4   ✳ 2 Chronicles 26:4

Teaching is only effective against a background of lives which are godly and full of integrity. Children will watch you carefully.

Heartsearch

Memories!

(Think about when you were under 11 for these questions.)

What are your best memories from childhood?

_____

_____

_____

What are your worst memories from childhood?

_____

_____

How would you describe yourself as a child?

☐ quiet ☐ happy ☐ obedient ☐ honest ☐ pleasant

☐ noisy ☐ unhappy ☐ rebellious ☐ deceitful ☐ unpleasant

Would you say that your parents taught you about God? ☐ yes ☐ no

Would you say that your parents were a good example to you? ☐ yes ☐ no

How would you describe your relationships with your parents as a child?

	very good	good	poor	very poor
With father	☐	☐	☐	☐
With mother	☐	☐	☐	☐

Have these relationships affected your life significantly? How?

_____

_____

What are your best memories about your parents?

_____

● Children should obey their parents

✻ Colossians 3:20

Why should children obey? ______________________________

✻ Proverbs 28:24

What should children not do? ______________________________

● Parents should discipline their children

✻ Proverbs 19:18

The Bible encourages us to discipline children effectively. To fail to do so is to neglect our responsibility and will have bad consequences for the children in our care. Why is discipline and corporal punishment recommended by the writer of the Proverbs?

Prov 13:24 ______________________________

Prov 22:15 ______________________________

Prov 23:13-14 ______________________________

Prov 29:15 ______________________________

Prov 29:17 ______________________________

✻ Hebrews 12:4-11

Why does God discipline us? ______________________________

____

✻ Ephesians 6:4 **✻ Colossians 3:21**

What do parents need to avoid? ______________________________

____

How well were you disciplined as a child?

Can you remember any particular occasions?

childhood

extra thought and discussion

• Adoption

Moses was adopted by Pharoah's daughter (Ex 2:5-10) and Esther was adopted by her uncle (Est 2:7).

Adoption is used in the Bible to illustrate the complete incorporation of individuals into the family of God with the full rights of natural children (John 1:12-13, Eph 1:5, Gal 3:26-4:7).

• Orphans

God has particular concern for orphans (often referred to as fatherless) (Deut 10:18, Ps 10:14, 27:10, 68:5, 146:9). He also commands us to care for them (Ex 22:22, Deut 26:12, James 1:27).

young person

This is a time of strength, beauty and idealism and can be used greatly in God's service.

● Young people who served God

✳ 2 Chronicles 34:1-8

Josiah's father and grandfather were both wicked kings who worshipped idols and neglected the true God. Josiah came to the throne when he was only eight years old. What did he do when he was

16 years old? _____

20 years old? _____

26 years old? _____

✳ 2 Chronicles 34:26-33

What character qualities are evident in Josiah?

_____

_____

✳ Luke 1:26-38

Imagine what must have passed through Mary's mind.

_____

How did she cope? _____

✳ Daniel 1:1-21   ✳ Daniel 3:1-30

How did Daniel and his three young friends stand out from the crowd?

_____

_____

What idols are there in today's culture that young people might need to resist worshipping?

Think!

● Advice and instruction to young people

Young people can be reckless and vulnerable. The Bible is full of advice and instruction on how to live and how not to live.

● Some things to do

Ex 20:12		☐
Lev 19:32		☐
Ps 119:9		☐
Prov 1:8-9		☐
Prov 2:1-8		☐
Prov 3:3-4		☐
Prov 4:23		☐
Eccl 12:1		☐
1 Tim 4:12		☐
Titus 2:6		☐

● Some things to avoid

Prov 1:10-15		☐
Prov 4:14-17		☐
Prov 4:24		☐
Prov 6:1-5		☐
Prov 6:23-29		☐
Prov 23:17		☐
Prov 23:20-21		☐
2 Tim 2:22		☐

In the boxes ☐ give yourself a score indicating how well you managed these things when you were young (bad-0-1-2-3-4-5-good).

You will see that the book of Proverbs is good reading for young people!

● Foolishness of young people

✱ **1 Kings 12:1-16** What was Rehoboam's foolishness?

_____

✱ **Luke 15:11-24** What was this young man's foolishness?

_____

● Make the connections

Commissioned as a young person by God	• David (1 Sam 17)	Resisted the sexual advances of an employer
Showed God's power when everybody else was afraid	• Elisha (1 Kings 19:19-21)	Loyal and loving to a mother-in-law
Lost by parents for three days	• Esther (Est 4:15-16)	Closed down his business to follow the man of God
Risked her life for her own people	• Jeremiah (Jer 1:6-8)	Got close to God with a man of God
Believed when everybody else doubted	• Jesus (Luke 2:44-52)	A girl who prophesied
Boldly spoke about God so that an employer was healed	• Joseph (Gen 39)	Waited for the older people to have their say before joining the debate
	• Joshua (Ex 33:7-11)	
	• Philip's daughter (Acts 21:9)	
	• Rhoda (Acts 12:12-17)	
	• Ruth (Ruth 1:1-18)	
	• Slave girl (2 Kings 5)	
	• Elihu (Job 32:1-5)	

The lives of many of these young people are worth further study.

● Honouring parents

✳ **Exodus 20:12**   ✳ **Ephesians 6:1-3**
This is a commandment with a promise. What is the promise?

_____

✳ **Proverbs 23:22**   How can we honour our parents?

_____

✳ **Proverbs 17:25**   What brings grief and bitterness to parents?

_____

✳ **Proverbs 23:24-25**   What brings joy and gladness to parents?

_____

✳ **John 19:25-27**   How did Jesus honour his mother as he was dying?

_____

Heartsearch   *Memories!*

(Think about when you were 12-25 for these questions.)

What are your best memories from when you were young?

_____

_____

What are your worst memories from when you were young?

_____

_____

How would you describe your own character, life and attitudes as a young person?

☐ teachable   ☐ godly   ☐ happy   ☐ fruitful   ☐ stable

☐ unteachable ☐ ungodly ☐ sad   ☐ unfruitful ☐ unstable

If you could re-live your youth, what would you like to change?

_____

How did you communicate with your parents when you were a young person?

	very well	well	badly	very badly
Father	☐	☐	☐	☐
Mother	☐	☐	☐	☐

How well have you honoured your parents?

	very well	well	badly	very badly
Father	☐	☐	☐	☐
Mother	☐	☐	☐	☐

Is there anything you can do about it now or in the future?

_____

guidance

We all make decisions every day. Some of these are of little importance, others have far reaching consequences for us and other people. As Christians we wish to make wise decisions in line with God's will.

● Why we need guidance

✳ **Proverbs 14:12**

What about our own ideas? _____

Human beings are fallible. Our judgment is flawed and we often make mistakes. We need God to guide us.

● God promises to guide us

Many times God says that he wishes to lead, guide and help us. Consider these promises:

✳ **Psalm 23:1-3, 32:8, 48:14**   ✳ **Isaiah 30:21, 42:16, 58:9-11**

● Receiving guidance

✳ **Proverbs 3:5-6**   What three things do we need to do?

- _____
- _____
- _____

What else is required?

✳ **Psalm 25:9** _____   ✳ **Isaiah 48:17-18** _____

Heartsearch

Do you really believe that God has your best interests at heart and that he can be fully trusted?_____

Are you prepared to consult your Father in all things and allow him to guide you - even if the answer might not be what you want?_____

✳ **Matt 26:39   Your will be done!**

● General guidance — the Bible

✴ Psalm 119:105   What is the word of God?

_____

There are many matters of guidance which can be easily resolved by reading the Bible. In it you will find guidelines for living and examples from people's lives. You will also learn more about the personality, character and will of God. Other methods of guidance can be checked against the written word of God.

● Conscience and wisdom

✴ Jeremiah 31:33-34

Where is the law of God under the new covenant? _____

✴ Romans 12:2

What can we do when our minds are renewed?_____

For the believer filled with the Holy Spirit, it should be possible to discover the will of God because of our relationship with him. This is often a clear but unspectacular knowledge of the right course of action.

● God speaks directly

✴ Acts 8:26-13:3   This passage is packed with guidance. Write the names of people guided in these ways (some in more than one way).

A voice   _____ ☐

A vision   _____ ☐

An angel   _____ ☐

The (Holy) Spirit   _____ ☐

Tick the boxes if you have experienced any of these.

Throughout the Bible it is normal for people to be guided supernaturally by dreams, visions, angels, signs and the voice of God.

Do you expect God to speak to you in these ways?

● Advice and counsel

✴ Proverbs 15:22

When do plans fail? _____

When do plans succeed? _____

14

✻ Proverbs 12:15

What kind of person listens to advice? _____

It is human nature to be independent and think that we know best. God has given us many people who are able to advise us — our parents, relatives, church leaders, friends, people at work, older people etc. It is important to take advice *before we make our decision and while the options are still open*. Include the advice of others in *your* decision making.

How good are you at taking advice?

☐ very good ☐ good ☐ poor ☐ very poor

Who are your main advisors in the big decisions of life?

Do you only ask advice from those whom you think will agree with you?

Heartsearch

● The prophetic word

A special kind of advice is the prophetic word. In the Bible we find kings and other people going to prophets to seek the word of the Lord for particular situations.

✻ 1 Samuel 9:1-20

Why did Saul go to Samuel? _____

What other guidance did Samuel give? _____

Think!

If you seek guidance from a prophet you might get a surprise like Saul did! It is always important to test prophetic advice against other ways of guidance. Prophets can be wrong like anybody else.

Have you ever been guided by a prophetic word? If so, when and how?

_____

✻ 1 Thessalonians 5:19-21   Four things we should do.

● _____   ● _____

● _____   ● _____

● Circumstances

✻ 1 Corinthians 16:8-9   ✻ 2 Corinthians 2:12-13   ✻ 1 Thess 2:18

God can guide us through events and through "open doors". We should be careful, however, with this kind of guidance or we may be pushed to and fro by circumstances. Sometimes the devil can hinder us and we may need to take a course of action in spite of the circumstances. We need wisdom and to include the many ways in which God guides.

How much do you seek God's guidance in your life?

Are you seeking guidance at the moment and can you put the ideas from this study into action?

guidance
extra thought and discussion

• Asking God for guidance

Don't be afraid to ask God for guidance. You will find many such requests in the Bible (Ps 25:4-5, 27:11, 43:3, 61:2, 143:7-10, 119:133, Jer 6:16).

• Conscience

Our conscience is our internal indicator of right and wrong (Rom 2:14-15). If we do right we have a clear conscience (Acts 24:16, 1 Peter 3:16) and if we do wrong we have a guilty conscience (Ps 51).

Unfortunately as sinful human beings our consciences can be weak (1 Cor 8:7), seared (1 Tim 4:2) or corrupted (Titus 1:15) and so they are not perfect indicators of right and wrong (Eph 4:17-19). Jesus came both to cleanse our guilty consciences by his death on the cross (Heb 10:19-22) and to correct our faulty consciences by the power of the Holy Spirit in our lives.

• Guidance by events

- **Circumstances** — These are the normal events of life happening around us which direct our lives (Josh 2:23-24, Ruth 2:2-3, Acts 6:1-4, 20:3).
- **Signs** — Signs are unusual, unlikely or supernatural events which convince us that God is directing us in a particular way (Ex 13:21-22, Judg 7:9-15).
- **Fleece** — This is named after Gideon's fleece (Judg 6:36-40). Guidance is sought by asking for a specific sign (Gen 24:10-27).
- **Vow** — A vow is a solemn promise made to God that if certain events take place then you will pursue a course of action (Gen 28:20-22). Vows should not be taken lightly (Deut 23:21-23, Judg 11:29-40, Jer 42:1-43:4).
- **Chance** — This is drawing lots, tossing a coin or using some other chance method to make a decision (1 Sam 14:36-42, Prov 16:33, Jonah 1:7, Acts 1:26) — not recommended! It is possible that the Urim and Thummim used by the priests in the Old Testament relied on this method (Ex 28:30, Num 27:21).

• Forbidden methods of guidance

Some methods of guidance are clearly forbidden (Lev 19:31, Deut 18:10-12, Is 8:19-20).

- Fortune telling, divination, omens
- Mediums, spiritists and consulting the dead
- Occult practices, witchcraft and sorcery

• Free choice and God's control

The Bible clearly teaches that God is in overall charge of the universe, yet within that we have our own free choice. This is hard for us to understand! God calls, rules and guides — we can choose to align our lives with his purposes or we can disobey and step outside God's will. We are responsible for our decisions and our choices.

- **God's control** — Ps 135:6, Rom 8:28-30, Eph 1:3-14, Gal 1:15, James 4:13-15
- **Our choice** — Josh 24:15, Deut 30:19
- **Both** — Prov 16:9, Acts 2:23

• Back on track - redemption

We make bad decisions for different reasons.

- In all good faith we sought guidance, believing at the time that the decision was right, but we were mistaken — we have a good God and can be sure that he will help us through our difficulties.
- Or it may be that we did not seek guidance from God or were rebellious in our decision — we need to repent of our actions and our lack of seeking God, then he will help us through our difficulties.

We may feel that we have made serious mistakes and have lost God's plan for our lives. But God is a God of redemption and restoration and is capable of transforming a dreadful error into something good. Reflect on David's sin with Bathsheba, how he repented, and the birth of Solomon (2 Sam 11-12). Plan A becomes plan B but it can be converted by God into another glorious plan A.

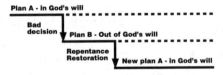

There is nothing that God cannot do!

• Other guidance verses

- **Inquiring of the Lord** — 1 Sam 23:1-6, 28:5-7, 30:7-8, 2 Sam 2:1-2, 5:17-25
- **The word of God** — Ps 19:7-11, Ps 119:97-104, 129-136, 2 Tim 3:16-17
- **The Holy Spirit** — John 16:13, Rom 8:14
- **Wisdom** — Prov 2:1-11, 1 Kings 3:4-15, James 1:5-6

work

● Work intended as a blessing

✳ **Genesis 2:2**

Who was the first worker in the Bible? _____

✳ **Genesis 1:27-28**   ✳ **Genesis 2:15**

What work was Adam given to do?

_____

_____

God is a worker and he made us to be workers like himself. Adam worked *with* God and *for* God. His work was *his calling from God.*

● Work became a burden

✳ **Genesis 3:17-19**

Why did work become a burden to Adam?

_____

The pleasure and fulfilment of work has been lost to many because of our sin. The evils of our society, hardship, exploitation, oppression, unfairness, dishonesty, corruption, abuse, poverty and unemployment have all contributed to a negative view of work. It is, however, still God's call for us to work and there can be fulfillment and blessing in work for believers.

✳ **Ecclesiastes 2:17-26**   Reflect on this passage.

What is your attitude to work?

☐ I enjoy it   ☐ I try to avoid it   ☐ I hate it

☐ I find it fulfilling   ☐ I find it tedious and boring

☐ I am looking for it   ☐ It is God's call for me

Think!

● Skills and God's purpose

✳ **Exodus 31:1-6** ✳ **Exodus 35:30-36:2**

What skills did God give to Bazalel and Oholiab?

_____

What were these men filled with? _____(35:31)

What other ability did they have? _____(35:34)

Sometimes God's purpose is less obvious - which of the following do you think applies to God's purpose in *your* work?

☐ To serve other people   ☐ To teach you patience and discipline

☐ To meet other people through your work and be a witness

☐ To provide for yourself, your family and the work of God

☐ To be a good influence in the world   ☐ To use your gifts and skills to the full

✳ **Mark 6:1-3** ✳ **1 Thessalonians 2:9** ✳ **Acts 18:3**

What job did Jesus do until he was about 30? _____

What did Paul do for a living? _____

Both were content to do ordinary jobs patiently even though they had other things on their minds! Less demanding jobs can be useful.

How well is your work matched to your gifts?

In the first column put your own assessment of your gifting in each skill on a scale 0-5. In the second column put the demands of your job for each skill again on a scale 0-5. In the last column put the difference between the other two columns. Finally add up the last column and put the total at the bottom.

Skill	Your gifting	Your work	Difference
Creative — planning, designing, inventing	____	____	____
Coordination — use of hands, feet, eyes, ears	____	____	____
Expression — speaking or writing	____	____	____
Social — interacting with other people	____	____	____
Knowledge — remembering information	____	____	____
Intellectual — analysing, reasoning, organising	____	____	____
Physical strength — manual work	____	____	____
Artistic — art, music etc	____	____	____

Total difference ____

Results: 0-8 excellent match, 9-16 good match, 17-24 some match, 25+ poor match

Many of us will be engaged in work which does not use all our skills. Those which are not used in our job may be used in other areas of our lives.

● Being a hard worker

In the Bible we are encouraged to work hard and not to be lazy — look at the consequences of idleness and hard work.

	Rewards of laziness	Reward of diligence
Prov 6:6-11	_____	
Prov 10:4	_____	_____
Prov 12:24	_____	_____
Prov 15:19	_____	_____
Prov 24:30-34	_____	
Prov 28:19	_____	_____
Eccl 10:18	_____	

✻ **Proverbs 26:13-16** What does the sluggard do? _____

_____

✻ **1 Thessalonians 4:11-12** Why should we work hard?

_____

✻ **2 Thessalonians 3:8-12** Who was a hard worker? _____

✻ **1 Timothy 5:8** Why should we work? _____

✻ **Exodus 18:13-18** Who worked too hard? _____

Think!

How would you describe yourself?

☐ lazy ☐ average ☐ work hard ☐ work too hard

Is there anything you should do about it?

● Being a good employee

There is also a lot in the Bible about how we should behave at work. Several of the following passages are about masters and slaves since this was a common situation in Bible times — many of the principles can be applied to employers and employees today.

✻ **Ephesians 6:5-8** ✻ **Colossians 3:22-25**

How should we work when we are not being watched? _____

Whom are we serving when we work? _____

✳ **Titus 2:9-10**   Why should we be polite, honest and trustworthy at work? _____

✳ **1 Timothy 6:1-2**   Why should we respect our earthly bosses?

_____

Why should we be careful if we have Christian bosses?

_____

✳ **1 Peter 2:18-20**   What can you learn from a bad boss?

_____

This does not mean that we should endure endless abuse but it does suggest ways of dealing with these problems in a godly way.

● Being a good boss

What aspects of being a good boss are highlighted in these passages?

Deut 5:14   _____

Deut 24:14-15   _____

Jer 22:13   _____

Eph 6:9   _____

Col 4:1   _____

How well do you relate to your

boss? _____

fellow workers? _____

employees? _____

work

extra thought and discussion

Full-time for God

Some people will be called to "full-time" Christian work (1 Tim 5:17-18). However we all need to see our whole lives as dedicated to God so in that respect we are all "full-time"! Read the book of Daniel and see how he was used in a "secular" job.

Philemon

Read this moving letter from Paul to Philemon asking him to take back his runaway slave.

Other discussion points

• **Ambition** — This can be bad if selfish (Phil 2:3). It is good to be successful if our motives are right..

• **Rights** — As a Christian do you have views on worker rights, trade unions and strike action?

• **Unemployed, disabled, retired** — How can the Christian community support those who are out of work for one reason or another?

possessions

● The true owner

✳ **Psalm 24:1**   Who is the true owner of everything? _____

✳ **Deuteronomy 8:17-18**
What should we remember about our possessions?

_____

✳ **1 Chronicles 29:10-16**
This is David's prayer after a very generous offering of materials to build the temple.

Have you ever realised that all your possessions really belong to God and that you are only a temporary steward? How can this change the way you live?

Think!

● Rich and poor

How to get rich!

Prov 3:9-10	_____
Prov 3:13-16	_____
Prov 10:4	_____
Prov 10:22	_____
Prov 22:4	_____
Deut 11:13-15	_____

How to become poor!

Prov 14:23	_____
Prov 21:5	_____
Prov 21:17	_____
Prov 22:16	_____
Prov 28:22	_____
Deut 11:16-17	_____

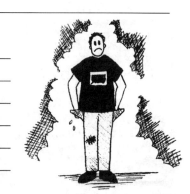

Wealth can be a reward from God for sensible and righteous living and poverty the result of foolishness and neglect of God. However it is not always as simple as this and sometimes the wicked prosper *(Job 21:4-16, Ps 73, Jer 12:1-2)* and godly people endure poverty *(Luke 16:19-31)*.

● Attitudes to possessions

✳ Proverbs 30:7-9

What is a snare of the rich? _____

What is a snare of the poor? _____

✳ 1 Timothy 6:6-10, 17-19

What should we be content with? _____

What are the snares of greed? _____

What is a root of all kinds of evil? _____

What should the rich not do? _____

What should the rich do? _____

✳ Mark 10:17-31

Why was it so hard to follow Jesus?

_____

✳ Luke 12:13-21

Why was this rich man a fool?

_____

Riches are temporary. When we die they will be passed on to others who will use them as they wish *(Psalm 39:6, Eccl 2:18-19)*.

✳ James 2:1-7 How should we treat rich and poor? _____

✳ James 5:1-6 What have these wicked rich people done?

● _____(v 3)

● _____(v 4)

● _____(v 5)

✳ Revelation 3:14-22 A rich church can have problems too!!

✳ Eccl 5:8-20 Reflect on this passage.

Heartsearch

What about you? Is your main aim to get rich? Do you trust in your possessions? Are you proud of them? Do you worship them? Are they a snare to you? Are you greedy and covetous? How can you lay up treasure in heaven?

22

● Giving

✳ **Leviticus 27:30-33**   ✳ **2 Chronicles 31:4-6**

What fraction is a tithe? _____

In the Old Testament, first fruits and tithes were considered to be God's and were given to the Levites and the poor.

✳ **Malachi 3:7-10**

How were these people robbing God?

_____

What was promised if they began to give?

_____

● How to give (complete the words)

S _ _ **r** _ _ _ _   (Matt 6:1-4)

R _ _ **u** _ _ _ _ _ _   (1 Cor 16:2)

G _ _ _ **r** _ _ _ _ _   (Ps 37:21,26)

C _ _ _ _ _ **f** _ _ _ _   (2 Cor 9:7)

S _ **c** _ _ **f** _ _ **i** _ _ _ _   (2 Cor 8:1-5, Lk 21:1-4)

C _ _ **p** _ _ _ _ **i** _ _ _ _ **t** _ _ _   (1 John 3:17, Matt 25:35, Deut 15:11)

How do you fare with the above list? Do you give to the work of God and to the poor? What is your level of giving in relation to your income?

☐ 1% ☐ 2% ☐ 5% ☐ 10% ☐ 15%

Can you make any changes?

● Integrity in managing possessions and money

What practices should be avoided? How do you fare?

Ex 18:21 _____   Deut 16:19 _____

Ps 37:21 _____   Eccl 7:7 _____

Prov 20:17 _____   Rom 13:6-7 _____

Ezek 18:8 _____

possessions

extra thought and discussion

• Tithing

Tithing goes back to Abraham who gave a tenth of his belongings (Gen 14:17-20, Heb 7:1-10) and the vow of Jacob at Bethel to return a tenth of all that God gave to him (Gen 28:20-22).

Each year the Israelites were to give a tenth of their crops and animals but this could be converted into money in certain circumstances (Lev 27:30-33, Deut 14:22-27). It was to be brought to Jerusalem with feasting before the Lord or shared with the Levites and the poor in their own towns (Deut 14:28-29). The Levites received the tithes of the people in return for their service to God and they in turn tithed to the priests (Num 18:21-32). As well as tithes there were freewill offerings and first fruits.

Jesus did not condemn the principle of tithing, but its abuse and the ritual observance of petty rules (Matt 23:23-24). Many Christians tithe their income to the work of God in their local church believing that it is a God-ordained level of giving in much the same way that taking one day off in seven is a God-ordained level of resting.

• Use of church money

- **The poor** — Jesus and his disciples had a joint fund which was used for the poor (John 12:4-6, 13:29) and after his death Christians continued to give to the poor (Acts 2:44-45, 4:32-37, 6:1-3).
- **Local pastors** — Those who devote themselves to the service of God should be well supported (1 Tim 5:17-18).
- **Travelling ministers** — Finance is required for missionaries and those who travel preaching the gospel (Phil 4:14-18).
- **Giving to other churches** — Rich churches can sometimes support poorer churches (Acts 11:27-30, Rom 15:25-26, 2 Cor 8:1-9:15).
- **Projects** — Money and possessions were given for the building of the tabernacle and temple (Ex 35:4-29, 1 Chron 29:1-9). Christian projects can be supported in a similar way today.

• Lending and borrowing

Although lending and borrowing is permitted in the Bible, it is generally seen as a great disadvantage to be a borrower (Prov 22:7). Debts are best avoided in the first place and should be paid off as quickly as possible (Rom 13:8). We should avoid putting up security for the debts of others (Prov 11:15).

Lenders are to be compassionate and not take advantage of their position (Deut 15:7-8, Matt 5:42). Vital items should not be kept as security for debts (Ex 22:26-27, Deut 24:6). Israelites were not permitted to charge interest to each other but could from foreigners (Deut 23:19-20). Every seven years all debts were to be cancelled (Deut 15:1-11). Every 50 years (Jubilee) all land was returned to its original owners (Lev 25). It is better to give than to lend (Luke 6:34-35). It is worth considering how these Biblical principles can be applied in the church and the world today.

• "Egyptian Gold"

When the Israelites left the slavery of Egypt, they took with them a lot of gold from the Egyptians (Ex 12:35-36). Later this gold was used in the construction of the tabernacle, the ark of the covenant etc (Ex 25:1-9). This begs the question whether it is right to use the systems and wealth of the world to fund the work of the kingdom of God. Note that Israelites were permitted to gain interest from loans to outsiders (Deut 23:20). The parables of the talents (Matt 25:14-30) and the shrewd manager (Luke 16:1-15) may also be relevant.

• Gambling

Gambling such as casinos, lotteries, raffles, pools, prize draws, betting etc are not mentioned in the Bible. Many Christians object to gambling because:

- It is poor stewardship of God's resources.
- It can be a very wasteful, addictive and destructive habit leading to poverty and degradation.
- The concept of 'luck' is not relevant to Christians.
- It appeals to greed and covetousness.
- Money should be obtained by work and other proper means.

It is worth considering whether competitions where no money or effort is invested should be considered as gambling. Also, is investment in the stock market a form of gambling?

• Insurance, savings, pensions

Christians vary in their attitudes to insurance policies. Some would argue that they represent trust in riches and that we should trust in the provision of God if trouble comes. Others see the value in contributing to a joint fund which then can help those who suffer loss.

Some Christians do not save and others object to their resources being invested in financial institutions which may be taking advantage of poor countries or fund unwholesome activities through share holding.

• Treasure

Is it appropriate for Christians to hoard expensive goods or collectors' items? Jesus said that your heart is where your treasure is (Matt 6:19-21). Your treasure in heaven is your own eternal life and that of those whom you help to faith in Jesus Christ (Phil 4:1). Store up treasure in heaven.

• Rich and poor in the Bible

- **Rich** — Abraham, Solomon, Job, Zaccheus, Joseph of Arimathea, Cornelius.
- **Poor people** — Jesus (Matt 8:20, 2 Cor 8:9), Paul (2 Cor 6:10), apostles (Acts 3:6).

eating

Food in the Bible

Many of the foods mentioned in the Bible are common in Mediterranean areas today.

- **Bread** — Bread was the main staple food made from various grains (wheat and barley), olive oil and yeast. Manna was eaten in the desert.
- **Fruit** — Apples, dates, figs, grapes, melons, pomegranates, olives, dried fruits.
- **Vegetables** — Beans, lentils, leeks, cucumbers, onions.
- **Meat and animal products** — Meat (beef, lamb or goat) was only eaten on special occasions. Fish was available near the sea or inland water. Birds (eg quail) and certain insects (eg locusts) were eaten and there is passing mention of cheese and eggs.
- **Seasoning** — Salt, herbs and spices were used to add flavour to food.
- **Delicacies** — Honey, almonds and pistachio nuts.
- **Drinks** — Water, wine, vinegar, milk, beer.

● Food - a gift from God

✳ Genesis 1:29

Who gave food to humans? _____

What kind of food did Adam and Eve eat?

_____

✳ Genesis 9:1-4

What other food did God give to Noah after the flood? _____

What restriction was there?

_____

✳ Psalm 104:14-15

Who makes our food? _____

What three staple foods are mentioned?

● _____ ● _____ ● _____

✳ Luke 9:17   ✳ Luke 22:19   ✳ Luke 24:30

What two things did Jesus do before he ate bread?

● _____   ● _____

What *three* ways can we pray about food?

Matt 6:11 _____

Ps 147:7-9 _____

1 Tim 4:3-5 _____

Thank you Lord

Think!

Do you acknowledge God as the provider of your food and do you regularly thank him for it?

● Meals

Eating meals together has always been a sign of friendship and fellowship. Meals, feasts and banquets also accompanied the making of covenants and other special occasions. What were these occasions?

Gen 26:28-31	_____	Judg 14:10	_____
Gen 40:20	_____	Est 2:17-18	_____
Ex 12:1-11	_____	Luke 5:27-32	_____
Ex 23:14-17	_____	Luke 15:23-24	_____
Lev 7:11-21	_____	Luke 22:14-23	_____

Eating together is an important part of normal family life.

● Hospitality

✳ 1 Peter 4:9 How should we offer hospitality? _____

✳ Luke 14:2-14 Whom should we invite to meals? _____

✳ Hebrews 13:2 Whom else should we invite? _____

✳ Proverbs 15:17 What should you do if you don't have much food?

Heartsearch

Do you consider it important to eat together with your family/household?

How do you rate your hospitality?

☐ very hospitable   ☐ hospitable

☐ rarely entertain guests   ☐ never entertain guests

Dr Tony's medical guide to fasting!

• Is fasting safe?

Fasting is generally safe provided fluid intake is continued (1-2 litres per day). It is not recommended for pre-school children, pregnant women, the elderly and those with diabetes — if in doubt consult your doctor.

• How does my body respond?

Your brain prefers to use glucose as a source of energy but your body supplies of this type of sugar run out after a few hours. Glucose is then manufactured from body protein, which is taken from muscles.

After a few days, less protein is sacrificed and fat becomes the main fuel. Unfortunately glucose cannot be made from fat so instead your brain has to rely on substances called "ketone bodies" which are produced in large quantities in the liver when fat is broken down. Only small amounts of ketone bodies are used up at a time and so they build up in the blood, causing it to become more acidic. Acetone may evaporate into the breath giving it a characteristic smell. These changes in body chemistry can be offset by the taking of drinks which contain sugar, eg sweet tea or coffee.

• Breaking a fast

To break a long fast, take small carbohydrate snacks at first which, when digested, give the body some sugars which stimulate a change in the level of hormones which have been controlling the adaptions. The perfectionist may wish at this stage to top up on the water-soluble vitamins B and C which are present in fruit and vegetables.

● Fasting ✳ Matthew 6:16-18

Jesus considered fasting to be a normal part of the life of his disciples.

How did he say we should fast? _____

Fasting in the Bible is not just a spiritual exercise for personal discipline but is linked with specific urgent matters. People fasted from 1 day to 40 days! Why did these people fast?

Deut 9:9-10	_____	Est 4:12-16	_____
Judg 20:26-28	_____	Ps 35:13-14	_____
1 Sam 31:11-13	_____	Dan 9:1-4	_____
1 Kings 19:3-18	_____	Jonah 3:1-10	_____
1 Kings 21:20-29	_____	Matt 4:1-4	_____
2 Chron 20:1-4	_____	Luke 2:36-38	_____
Ezra 8:21-23	_____	Acts 13:1-3	_____

Have you ever fasted? ☐ Yes ☐ No

Are there things for which you might fast? ☐ Yes ☐ No

Would you like to see fasting as part of your life? ☐ Yes ☐ No
(Read Isaiah 58:1-9.)

● Gluttony ✳ Ecclesiastes 6:7 ✳ Philippians 3:19

How can over-indulgence in food be a form of idolatry?

_____

✳ **Proverbs 25:16** Over-eating is a lack of self-control which can be symptomatic of a similar lack in other areas of life. Gluttony is often included with other serious sins.

● Alcohol ✳ Proverbs 20:1

✳ **Proverbs 23:19-21, 29-35**

✳ **Proverbs 31:4-7** ✳ **Isaiah 28:7-8**

What dangers are mentioned here?

_____

_____

_____

Addictions

The Bible's comments on alcohol can be extended to the use of other addictive substances (including drugs and tobacco). Here are some reasons why Christians avoid addiction.

- You waste money and God's resources.
- You can damage your body which is the temple of the Holy Spirit.
- You can damage your mind and emotions.
- Being drunk, high or stoned prevents you from functioning correctly or serving God and your behaviour may be degrading.
- You can cause physical and emotional damage and sorrow to other people by your behaviour.
- It can lead to sin in other areas of life.
- You may engage in illegal activities.
- Much time can be wasted in finding substances.
- It is a very self-centred activity.
- You are in bondage to a substance or a habit.

✳ **1 Corinthians 6:9-10**   ✳ **Galatians 5:19-21**   ✳ **Luke 21:34-36**

What will happen to drunkards? _____

● **Illegal substances**   ✳ **Genesis 3:1-19**

What did Eve hope to gain from the fruit? _____

What was the result of eating the fruit?

Heartsearch

_____

Have you any addictions? Who can help you overcome them (Matt 4:1-4, Heb 4:14-16)?

eating

extra thought and discussion

• Clean and unclean food

The Old Testament laws about clean and unclean animals make good medical sense. They mainly advise against eating carnivores high in the food chain and disease-carrying animals (Lev 11:1-47, Deut 14:3-21). These laws are relaxed for Gentile Christians (Acts 10:9-16, Acts 15:19-21).

• Vegetarianism

Eating of meat is acceptable in the Bible. Animals were used for sacrifice and animal products were used widely. There is no need to be vegetarian but you may choose to be so. We should avoid judging each other on these personal preferences (Dan 1:11-16, Rom 14:1-23, 1 Tim 4:3-5).

• Abstention from alcohol

Fermented drinks were consumed in Bible times but there are warnings about drunkenness. Drinking in moderation is permissible. Some people were called by God to abstain, others chose to do so. We should not judge (Lev 10:9, Num 6:1-4, Deut 29:6, Judges 13:2-5, Ezek 44:21, Dan 1:8-16, Jer 35:1-19, Luke 1:13-17, Rom 14:21).

• Eating disorders

Some modern eating disorders can be driven by a desire to change body mass and shape to become more attractive or acceptable in a society dominated by images presented in advertising and the media. Those with *anorexia nervosa* have an unrealistic view of their own weight, believing that they are overweight when they are not. Self-starvation can lead to other complications. Those with *bulimia nervosa*, obsessed with their body mass and lacking in self-control, engage in cycles of binge eating and induced vomiting and purging. Solutions to these disorders can be found in rejecting popular views of acceptable shape, and adopting a good self-image

and a realistic target for body mass.

• Dr Tony's guide to weight watching

Doctors often use the Body Mass Index (BMI). Your BMI is your weight in kilograms divided by your height in metres squared.

Serious low — Seriously undernourished (BMI=15).

OK low — Good weight for light-frame person, below this is underweight (BMI=20).

OK high — Good weight for heavy-frame person, above this is overweight (BMI=25).

Serious high — Anything above this is considered to be seriously overweight (BMI=31).

height cm	Serious low kg	OK low kg	OK high kg	Serious high kg
142	30	40	51	63
147	33	43	54	67
152	35	46	58	72
157	37	50	62	77
163	40	53	66	82
168	42	56	70	87
173	45	60	75	92
178	47	63	79	98
183	50	67	84	104
188	53	71	88	110
193	56	75	93	116
ft,in	**st,lb**	**st,lb**	**st,lb**	**st,lb**
4,8	4,11	6,5	7,14	9,12
4,10	5,2	6,12	8,8	10,8
5,0	5,7	7,4	9,2	11,5
5,2	5,12	7,11	9,11	12,1
5,4	6,3	8,5	10,6	12,13
5,6	6,9	8,12	11,1	13,10
5,8	7,1	9,6	11,10	14,8
5,10	7,7	9,13	12,6	15,6
6,0	7,13	10,7	13,2	16,5
6,2	8,5	11,2	13,13	17,3
6,4	8,11	11,10	14,9	18,3

knowledge

● The universe and nature

✳ Psalm 19:1-2

What do the heavens declare? _____

What do the skies proclaim? _____

✳ Job 9:9

Which three
constellations are
mentioned here?
Which are they?
Can you find them
in the sky?

 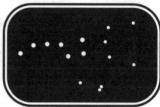 

_____ _____ _____

✳ Job 38:1-39:30

What point is God making to Job about creation and nature? _____

_____

✳ Job 40:1-5 ✳ Job 42:1-6

What should our response be to the wonders of nature? _____

✳ Romans 1:20

What does the universe tell us about God? _____

✳ Genesis 2:8-14

Which things are mentioned in this passage that human beings find beautiful or enjoyable?

_____

Since we are made in the image of God we are able to enjoy the things which he has made (*Ecclesiastes 3:11*). We may find people beautiful too (*Genesis 29:17, 1 Samuel 16:12, Esther 1:11*).

Do you ever stop and look at the universe and the world which God has made? Do they fill you with awe and wonder (Psalm 8:3-4, Revelation 4:11)?

What things do you enjoy most?

‑‑‑‑‑‑‑‑‑‑‑‑‑‑‑‑‑‑‑‑‑

✳ **Proverbs 6:25**   ✳ **2 Samuel 11:2-5**

What danger is associated with beautiful people?

‑‑‑‑‑‑‑‑‑‑‑‑‑‑‑‑‑‑‑‑‑

✳ **Joshua 7:19-23**

What danger is associated with beautiful things? ‑‑‑‑‑‑‑‑‑

✳ **Romans 1:25**   ✳ **Deuteronomy 17:3**   ✳ **Isaiah 47:13-15**

What danger is associated with appreciation of nature?

‑‑‑‑‑‑‑‑‑‑‑‑‑‑‑‑‑‑‑‑‑

Are these dangers still in the world today?

● Science and technology

✳ **Genesis 1:28**   ✳ **Genesis 2:15**   ✳ **Psalm 8:5-8**   ✳ **Psalm 115:16**

Science

- The first step in science is naming things. Animals, plants, parts of animals and plants, rocks, stars, cells, atoms, parts of atoms etc. We analyse and measure nature.
- The second step is understanding how the different parts of the world and universe work together. We formulate scientific laws.
- The third step is using this knowledge to enable us to control the world around us, make new materials, medicines, tools, machines etc.

What is our job on the earth?

‑‑‑‑‑‑‑‑‑‑‑‑‑‑‑‑‑‑‑‑‑

✳ **Genesis 2:19-20**

What was one of Adam's early scientific jobs?

‑‑‑‑‑‑‑‑‑‑‑‑‑‑‑‑‑‑‑‑‑

✳ **Genesis 4:22**

Who was the first engineer in the Bible?

‑‑‑‑‑‑‑‑‑‑‑‑‑‑‑‑‑‑‑‑‑

Good   **Bad**

What do you think of the scientific efforts of human beings? Which are good and which are bad?

● Poetry, singing and music

Much of the Bible is poetry. Hebrew poetry depended on *rhythm* not *rhyme* and it would sometimes be sung. Musical instruments were used to accompany singing, to celebrate, to mourn and to bring encouragement and comfort (*1 Samuel 16:14-23, 2 Kings 3:14-19*).

What were the occasions of the following songs?

2 Chron 5:11-13 _____   Ps 98:4-6 _____

Ex 15:1-18 _____   Col 3:16 _____

Ps 45 _____   Acts 16:25 _____

2 Sam 1:17-27 _____   Song of Songs _____

Think!

What are the main themes of modern songs today?

_____

What kind of songs and music do you like?

_____

Are there kinds of songs and music which you think are bad or harmful? Why?

_____

✳ **Revelation 5:9-13** Where is this song being sung? _____

✳ **Zephaniah 3:17** Who is singing? _____

✳ **Psalm 150** List the instruments in this Psalm.

_____

> **David** is the most famous musician in the Bible. He sang, played instruments, wrote songs and organised musicians and singers for the worship of God (1 Chronicles 25:1-8).

● Literature and history

The Bible itself is literature and history. Careful written records and historical accuracy were valued greatly in Bible times (*Luke 1:1-4*).

✳ **Daniel 2:20-21**   ✳ **Acts 17:26** Who is in charge of history? _____

History is the story of mankind's foolishness and God's plan to put things right and bring salvation.

✳ **1 Corinthians 15:3-4**

What are the most important historical facts for mankind?

_____

What kind of literature do you like reading?

_____

Are there any kinds of literature which would be
inappropriate or harmful for a Christian to read?

● Art

Men and women have always enjoyed making beautiful, ornamental
and significant objects from the materials around them. In the Bible we
find metal, wood, fabrics, leather, ivory, stone, paper, clay, precious
stones and dyes used to produce paintings, carvings, sculptures, pottery
and embroidery. See Solomon's temple (*2 Chronicles 2:1-4:22*).

✳ **Exodus 20:4-6**　　✳ **Deuteronomy 27:15**　　✳ **Isaiah 44:6-20**

What are the dangers in making images and statues?

_____

_____

Are there other dangers in art?

_____

Are there any types of art which you are particularly
fond of?

_____

● True wisdom and knowledge

✳ **2 Chronicles 1:7-12**　　✳ **James 1:5-7**

How do we get wisdom? _____

✳ **1 Kings 4:29-34**

What kinds of wisdom did Solomon get? _____

✳ **Job 28**　　✳ **Proverbs 1:7**　　✳ **Proverbs 8**

What is the beginning of wisdom and knowledge?

_____

✳ **Philippians 3:4-8**

Paul was educated and cultured with lots of worldly knowledge. He
counted all this rubbish compared with one thing. What was it?

_____

✳ **1 Corinthians 1:17-2:16**

Worldly wisdom does not lead to knowing God. What is the clue to
finding godly wisdom?

_____

rest

work

tired ⟳ refreshed

rest

Human beings and nature generally are designed for a cycle of work and rest. This operates on an hourly, daily, weekly and yearly basis.

● Peaceful sleep is a blessing from the Lord

✳ **Psalm 3:3-6**   ✳ **Psalm 4:7-8**

Why can we sleep in peace? _____

✳ **Psalm 121**   Who never goes to sleep? ____

✳ **Proverbs 3:21-26**

How can we sleep sweetly?

I will lie down and sleep in peace

_____

✳ **Psalm 127:1-2**   Don't overwork — it is God's will for us to sleep.

● Refreshment in the night

Sometimes God will use the night hours for our guidance and refreshment. What is happening in these passages?

Gen 28:10-17 _____	Ps 63:6-8 _____
Ps 119:62 _____	Ps 149:5 _____
Luke 6:12 _____	Acts 16:9-10 _____

● Hindrances to sleep

Sleep can be hindered by various factors - some good and some bad.

1 Sam 15:10-11_____	Job 7:4-5 _____
Ps 132:2-5 _____	Prov 6:1-4 _____
Eccl 2:22-23 _____	Eccl 5:12 _____
SS 3:1 _____	Is 48:22 _____

Heartsearch

What is your sleep pattern like?

Do you sleep soundly?

Do you draw close to God at night?

Are there hindrances to your sleep?

● Sabbath

The word "sabbath" comes from a Hebrew word meaning to cease.

✳ Genesis 2:2-3

Who was the first person to keep a sabbath? _____

The idea of resting one day in seven was established by God at creation.

✳ Exodus 20:8-11

The principle of the sabbath day is so important that it is included in the Ten Commandments. Which number commandment is it? _____

What is special about the sabbath day? (v 8 and 11) _____

What do you think this means?

_____

To whom was the sabbath day devoted?

(v 10) _____

Who should rest on the sabbath?

_____

> **Maker's Instruction Manual: Section 4**
>
> • **Maintenance**
>
> Careful maintenance will ensure that the human body and mind run smoothly.
>
> An essential part of regular maintenance is to rest from work one day in seven.

✳ Luke 4:16

What did Jesus usually do on the sabbath?

_____

✳ Mark 2:23-3:6

For whom was the sabbath made? _____

But who is lord of the sabbath? _____

What work is allowed on the sabbath? _____

Do you manage to take one day in seven off from work (this may be irregular if you have shift work or work in essential services)?

How do you spend your day off?

Think!

_____

Could you do more to devote the day to God? _____

✳ Isaiah 58:13-14

What is the reward of those who keep the sabbath? _____

● Holidays in Israel

✳ Leviticus 23   ✳ Numbers 28-29   ✳ Deuteronomy 16

The Israelites had certain days to rest from work. These days were to remember God's deliverance and his continued provision for his people. Can you find the names of these feasts? Put a tick in the box for those which were compulsory.

14th-21st of first month _____ ☐

7 weeks (50 days) after first sheaf _____ ☐

1st day of seventh month _____ ☐

10th day of seventh month _____ ☐

15th-22nd of seventh month _____ ☐

What activities were carried out at these feasts?

_____

_____

Think!

How much holiday do you take a year?

How do you spend it?

Is there any way you could devote it more to God?

● Recreation and leisure

For some a holiday involves relaxing, for others it involves activity – a change is as good as a rest! What activities do you like doing to "re-create" yourself?

☐ rest   ☐ cafes and bars   ☐ cinema

☐ theatre   ☐ television   ☐ shopping

☐ reading   ☐ chatting with friends

☐ visiting your family   ☐ praying

☐ reading the Bible   ☐ playing sport

☐ hobbies   ☐ sea and beach

☐ computing   ☐ walking around town

☐ listening to music   ☐ walking in the countryside   ☐ watching sport

☐ visiting historic places   ☐ going to large events   ☐ travelling   ☐ eating

Other_____

● Retreat

✱ Mark 6:30-32

Many find it helpful to spend some time quietly away
from their busy routines to rest and review their aims
and objectives in life. Have you ever done this? Could
you organise it somehow?

● God's rest for our souls

God's rest is not inactivity but it is a state of peace knowing the love and
security of God. You can be very busy but enjoying God's rest!

✱ Matt 11:28 Who can give you rest for your soul? _____

✱ Hebrews 3:7-4:11 What will prevent us entering this rest?

_____

_____

✱ Exodus 33:14

What will ensure God's rest? _____

✱ Psalm 23:2-3

What does God do for us as we rest? _____

✱ Isaiah 40:28-31

How can we renew our strength?

_____

---

rest

extra thought and discussion

• Sabbath

For the Israelites in Old Testament times, the
sabbath was more than a creation ordinance, it was
also a special *sign of the covenant* between God
and his people (Ex 31:12-18, Deut 5:12-15). The
sabbath principle is also evident in the "sabbath
year" when the land rested and the "jubilee year" (Ex
23:10-11, Lev 25, Deut 15).

By the time of Jesus, the Jewish leaders had
developed the sabbath laws into a detailed list of
petty rules which destroyed the spirit of the law.
Jesus did not object to the principle of the sabbath
but to the pedantic interpretation of the letter of the
law. To illustrate this he honoured the sabbath day
but intentionally did things which infringed the
burdensome rules of the religious leaders of his
time.

There seems to be no constraint on Gentile
Christians to keep the Jewish sabbath (Col 2:16) but
the principle of one day's rest in seven stands as a
God-given level of rest.

• Saturday or Sunday?

Because Jesus was raised from the dead on the first
day of the week, this soon became a special day for
Christians when they would meet together and break
bread (Acts 20:7, 1 Cor 16:2). Early Jewish believers
would also continue to keep the sabbath as the last
day of the week (Saturday) but for Gentile believers
the first day of the week (Sunday) became the day
off from work and was eventually called the *Lord's
Day*.

love

(Father love Son Spirit)

● God is love

✳ **1 John 4:16**

Love is an essential part of God's nature and is the basis of relationships within God himself.

God's love

Look up the verses and write words in this box to describe God's love.

✳ **Exodus 15:13**

✳ **Exodus 34:6**

✳ **Deuteronomy 7:9**

✳ **1 Chronicles 16:34**

✳ **Psalm 31:21**

✳ **Psalm 36:5**

✳ **Psalm 36:7**

✳ **Psalm 89:24**

✳ **Psalm 108:4**

✳ **Psalm 145:8**

✳ **Jeremiah 31:3**

✳ **Lamentations 3:22**

✳ **John 3:16** ✳ **Romans 5:8**

How has God shown his love to all human beings?

_____

Love is giving yourself for someone else even if they don't deserve it. This is what God did for us in Jesus. This is the main message of the Bible.

Heartsearch

✳ **Romans 8:37-39** ✳ **1 John 3:1**

Do you know the love of God deep in your heart? Are you secure in the knowledge that you are a child of your Father God, that he will care for you throughout your life and that you will spend eternity with him?

● Greatest commandments

✴ Mark 12:28-33

What is the greatest commandment?

_____

What is the second greatest commandment?

_____

✴ John 13:34-35

How should people know that we are Christians?

_____

✴ John 14:15-24

See how our relationship with Jesus, the Father and the Holy Spirit are closely connected with our level of love.

What is the proof that we really love Jesus and our Father?

_____

✴ John 15:9-17

What is the greatest proof of our love for others?

_____

● Love one another

✴ 1 John 3:11-24

How can we know that we have passed from death to life (v 14)?

_____

How should our love be shown (v 16-18)?

_____

What are God's commands (v 23)?

1) _____

2) _____

✴ 1 John 4:7-21

How did God show his love for us (v 9-10)?

_____

How can you live in God and God live in you (v 15-16)?

1) _____

2) _____

What is the test that we truly love God (v 19-20)?

_____

✳ Matthew 25:31-46

What practical things can you do to love God and other people?

_____

_____

_____

● Love defined

✳ 1 Corinthians 13:1-13

This is probably the most well-known passage in the Bible about love. It illustrates how love is so fundamental to the Christian life that without it even powerful and dramatic gifts are useless. Verses 4-7 form a definition of love. Give your love a score from 1 (poor) to 5 (good). Circle the number.

1 2 3 4 5 is patient	1 2 3 4 5 is kind
1 2 3 4 5 does not envy	1 2 3 4 5 does not boast
1 2 3 4 5 is not proud	1 2 3 4 5 is not rude
1 2 3 4 5 is not self-seeking	1 2 3 4 5 is not easily angered
1 2 3 4 5 keeps no record of wrongs	1 2 3 4 5 does not delight in evil
1 2 3 4 5 rejoices in the truth	1 2 3 4 5 always protects
1 2 3 4 5 always trusts	1 2 3 4 5 always hopes
1 2 3 4 5 always perseveres	1 2 3 4 5 never fails

✳ Philippians 2:1-8

What aspects of love are highlighted here?

_____

_____

✳ Colossians 3:12-14   ✳ 1 Peter 3:8-9

Consider your love for your Christian brothers and sisters. Are there things you can change in your attitudes or actions to express God's love more fully to Christian friends?

● Love your neighbour   ✳ Luke 10:25-37

For the Jews listening to this story it would have been a surprise for the Samaritan to help the injured man. Why *(John 4:9)*?

Are there needy people in your community whom no-one else helps whom you could show love to?

How could you set about it?

● Love your enemy   ✳ Luke 6:27-36   ✳ Romans 12:9-21

What should we do for our enemies?

_____

_____

Heartsearch

Do you have enemies? Who are they? How can you show love to them (Prov 24:17)?

● Love for Jesus

✳ John 13:36-38   ✳ John 18:15-27   ✳ John 21:15-17

How many times did Peter deny knowing Jesus? _____

How many times did Jesus ask Peter if he loved him? _____

Heartsearch

Even after Peter's failure, Jesus graciously drew Peter back to himself. Peter proved his love for Jesus by his life of bold witness and service.

As a Christian, how much do you love Jesus? Is he your first love?

---

love

extra thought and discussion

• Love and trust

Love should not be confused with trust. Although we are commanded to love everybody, we are not commanded to trust everybody. Some people who we love dearly we may never be able to trust. In fact the Bible warns us against trusting in people too much because we will be disappointed (Jer 17:5, Ps 146:3-4). Jesus loved everybody he met but he did not always trust them (John 2:23-25).

We need to seek to become trustworthy people. Trust can be earned through our love, honesty and reliability. Good two-way human relationships need a high degree of trust in order to operate effectively.

God is 100% loving, honest, reliable and trustworthy and we are encouraged many times in the Bible to put our trust in him (Ps 118:8, Ps 125:1, Prov 3:5).

friendship

● Good friends

✷ **Proverbs 17:17**   What does a friend do?

_____

✷ **Ecclesiastes 4:9-12**
Why is it good to have a friend?

_____

_____

_____

✷ **Proverbs 27:6**   ✷ **Proverbs 27:9**
How can good friends help you?

_____

✷ **Luke 15:6** ✷ **Luke 15:9**
What else can they do? _____

✷ **Proverbs 22:11**   How do we make friends?

_____

✷ **Proverbs 11:13**   How do we lose friends?

_____

Staying friends

Here is a list of qualities which help to maintain friendships. Tick the *five* which are most important to you.

☐ Honesty
☐ Trust
☐ Apology
☐ Forgiveness
☐ Tolerance
☐ Love
☐ Support
☐ Encouragement
☐ Help
☐ Sympathy
☐ Confidentiality
☐ Loyalty
☐ Communication
☐ Faithfulness
☐ Reliability

✷ **Psalm 119:63**   What kind of person makes a good friend?

_____

Think!

Who are *your* best friends?

_____

Are you a good friend to others?

● Loyalty

✳ Proverbs 20:6, 27:10

Loyal and lasting friendships are commended in the Bible.

✳ 1 Samuel 18:1-4, 20:41-42

David and Jonathan enjoyed a close covenant friendship which they maintained even in the most difficult circumstances. David fulfilled his promises even after the death of Jonathan (*2 Samuel 9:1-13*).

✳ Ruth 1:16-18

This is a beautiful story of loyal friendship across generations of Ruth and her mother-in-law Naomi.

● Friends of Jesus - friends of God

Jesus often referred to people as his friends and indeed he was accused of being a *friend of sinners (Matt 11:19)*. Jesus also had close friends.

✳ Luke 8:51 ✳ Luke 9:28 Which three apostles were close to Jesus?

_____

✳ John 13:23, 19:26, 20:2, 21:7, 21:20-24

Who do you think was the disciple whom Jesus loved? _____

✳ John 11:1-6 Who were these other three good friends of Jesus?

_____

✳ John 15:13-15 How can we be friends of Jesus?

_____

✳ Exodus 33:11 ✳ 2 Chronicles 20:7

Who were friends of God?

Think!

_____

Do you consider God and Jesus to be your friend?

● False friends

✴ Proverbs 19:4   ✴ Proverbs 19:6-7

What is a common cause of false friendship?

_____

● Bad friends

✴ 1 Corinthians 15:33

Some friends may not be good for you. Whom should we avoid?

Deut 13:6-8	_____	Prov 13:20	_____
Ps 1:1	_____	Prov 16:29	_____
Ps 26:4	_____	Prov 22:24-25	_____
Ps 101:7	_____	Prov 23:20	_____
Prov 4:14-17	_____	Prov 24:1	_____
Prov 5:8	_____	Prov 28:7	_____
Prov 12:26	_____	Eph 5:5-7	_____

✴ 1 Corinthians 5:9-11

Who might be the most dangerous kind of friend for a Christian?

_____

✴ John 17:15-19

Think about the friends you have. Are some harmful to you?

How do you relate to ungodly friends – do they draw you away from God or do you draw them nearer to God as Jesus did?

● Unhelpful friends

✴ Job 2:11-13   What were the names of Job's friends?

_____

✴ Job 6:14-17, 12:4, 19:13-22, 42:7-10

Job's friends began by sympathising but ended up criticising him. With all their words, theories and advice they were little comfort to suffering Job. He felt forlorn and friendless.

Beware of being a "Job's comforter"!

● Losing friends - broken relationships

One of the most distressing experiences of life is to lose a close friend. Those who have been the best friends can become the worst enemies since they can use what they know about you against you.

✳ Proverbs 16:28 ✳ Proverbs 17:9

What can be the cause of lost friendships? _____

✳ Psalm 31:9-13, 38:9-12, 41:7-9, 55:12-14, 55:20-21, 88:8, 109:1-5

Describe some of David's feelings of rejection.

_____

_____

✳ Matthew 26:14-16 ✳ Matthew 26:47-50

Even Jesus suffered betrayal from a friend.

How did Jesus address Judas after he betrayed him with a kiss?

_____

● Restoring friendships

Communication, apology, forgiveness and putting away the past are all helpful in restoring broken friendships. Are there friendships that you could restore (Psalm 133:1)?

friendship

extra thought and discussion

• Physical contact

It is normal in the Bible that relatives and good friends express their love for each other in brief affectionate contact such as an embrace or a kiss (Gen 33:4, Acts 20:37, Rom 16:16, 1 Pet 5:14).

There is however no place for sexual intimacy between friends. This is reserved for the covenant relationship of heterosexual marriage. Sex before marriage, even for engaged couples, is not appropriate for Christians (see Units 13 and 14).

• Paul and his friends

Paul had many friends who worked alongside him and who offered him hospitality as he travelled around (Rom 16:3-16, Col 4:14-15, Philm 1:1). His friends were male and female, old and young. In 1 Tim 5:1-2 he explains how we should treat our friends of various ages.

In his letters he often refers to the people he is addressing as "dear friends" (New International Version). This is a translation of the Greek word *agapetos* which means "the one I love" or "beloved". The word more usually used for "friend" in the New Testament is the Greek word *philos*.

Paul also had enemies and at times felt abandoned by his friends (2 Tim 4:9-18).

• Other Bible verses

Many or few friends? — Prov 18:24

Friendship with the world — James 4:4

Job's friend — Job 16:18-21

single

● Definitions

✳ Genesis 2:18

In Bible times the normal expectation was for men and women to be married. However in any society there are adults who are not married and are single – this may or may not be out of choice.

● It is good to be single

✳ 1 Corinthians 1:1, 7:8, 7:25-35

Who is the single person writing this letter? _____

What can married people expect (v 28)?

_____

What are married people concerned about? _____

What can single people devote themselves to? _____

A single person may have more freedom, time, flexibility and money to serve God.

Biblical marital status

• **Pre-marriage singles** — Young adults living in their parents' home. They do not have sexual relations and are expected to be virgins (Deut 22:13-21).

• **Betrothed, engaged or pledged to be married** — Single adults living with parents but their marriage partner has been chosen. They do not have sexual relations with their betrothed. The betrothal contract was almost as strong as marriage and was rarely reversed (Matt 1:18-25).

• **Married** — Men and women in a covenant relationship who have sexual relations (see Unit 14).

• **Post-married singles** — Adults who are widowed or divorced. Widows often went back to their parental families (Ruth 1:8-9).

• **Remarried** — Often widows married brothers or other close relatives of their husbands (Ruth 3:1-4).

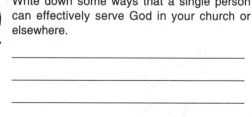

Write down some ways that a single person can effectively serve God in your church or elsewhere.

_____

_____

_____

_____

● Single and content - do not intend to marry

✻ 1 Corinthians 7:1, 7:7, 7:37 ✻ Matthew 19:10-12

Why do some people renounce marriage? ______________________

Some people are called to an unmarried, celibate state. Paul, Jeremiah *(Jeremiah 16:1-2)* and Jesus are examples of people who were called to be single because of their particular task for God. Paul was able to undertake very dangerous journeys and risk his life in the cause of the gospel because he did not have family responsibilities *(Luke 14:20, 18:29-30)*. Those called to celibacy can plan long term service for God.

✻ Mark 1:29-30 ✻ 1 Corinthians 9:5 ✻ 1 Timothy 4:1-4

Which apostle *was* married? ______________________

Permanent singleness is a call for some people but not for everybody.

● Single and content - but expect to marry

✻ 1 Corinthians 7:17-28

For many, singleness is a temporary state and their expectation is to marry at some time in the future. Those who are content will be able to devote themselves to God's service and use their freedom to full advantage. They may feel able to commit themselves to short term service for God.

✻ Acts 21:9

What did these unmarried girls do? ______________________

● Single and frustrated

Some single people feel very frustrated at being single and desire the intimate friendship afforded by marriage.

✻ 1 Corinthians 7:1-2, 7:8-9, 7:36-38 ✻ 1 Timothy 5:11-15

What should you do if you are frustrated? ______________________

If you are single - which of the above categories best fits you?

____

What short term opportunities for service for God are you aware of for single people? What is your experience of these?

● Loneliness

God made us to enjoy company and friendship. This is ideally fulfilled in marriage *(Genesis 2:18-24)* and it is only natural that single people will feel lonely from time to time. God has provided many ways to support single people.

● Friends

Friends of all ages, married, single and both genders can be a great encouragement (see Unit 11). Groups of people can have great fun together and this is a good setting for developing friendships, caring and praying for each other.

● Family ✳ Psalm 68:5-6

What does God do with lonely people? _____

As well as natural families, the whole family of God is able to provide help and support for single people.

How well do you provide friendship and a family backup for single people in your church or whom you know from work or other areas of life? Think about young singles, single parents, divorced, widowed etc.

Is there more you could do to help?

● Devotion to God's work ✳ Luke 2:36-37

What did this single person devote herself to? _____

Devotion to the work of God can take your attention away from yourself and any loneliness.

● God's presence and love

✳ **Psalm 139:7-10** ✳ **Isaiah 41:10** ✳ **Matthew 28:20** ✳ **John 14:18**

The Bible is packed with promises of the presence of God. This is the best and most permanent antidote to loneliness! He is always with you!

✳ **Deut 10:18** ✳ **Psalm 42:8** ✳ **John 13:1** ✳ **Rev 19:6-8, 21:1-2**

Even though we may not experience intimate human love, we can learn to love our Father and Jesus in an intimate way. We may not marry in this life but all believers are promised to be married in eternity.

Who is the bride?_____Who is the groom? _____

● Finding a spouse

Look at the following marriages in the Bible and decide if they are arranged marriages or love marriages. Circle A or L.

Ref	Person		
Gen 21:21	_____	A	L
Gen 24:1-67	_____	A	L
Gen 26:34-35	_____	A	L
Gen 29:15-18	_____	A	L
Judg 14:1-11	_____	A	L

Think!

What is your opinion of these ways of meeting your spouse? Do you think God can use them both? What is your experience? What do you think of organisations which introduce singles to each other?

Heartsearch

Man meets woman

There are two main systems in the world for finding a suitable husband or wife.

● Arranged marriage

Your spouse is found by your parents. You may meet the person briefly before you get married but you probably do not know them.

Advantages — You will not be left unmarried. Good parents will be very careful in choosing a suitable spouse and will usually go ahead only with your agreement. Your parents will be very committed to and supportive of your marriage since they have arranged it. You may make more effort to develop love for your spouse.

Disadvantages — You do not know the person you are getting married to and you may not like them. There is no way of testing the relationship.

● Love marriage

You meet someone and are attracted. You spend time with them and decide you love them and wish to marry them. You consult or inform your parents.

Advantages — You are able to test the friendship to see if you get on well together. You know the person you are getting married to.

Disadvantages — You may never meet anyone suitable and so remain single. There is a danger that infatuation and sexual attraction are mistaken for love and that these weaken in marriage. Your parents may not be supportive of the marriage.

Are you single? (or remember when you were single)

What do/did you find most difficult?

What do/did you enjoy most?

single

extra thought and discussion

● Problems with being single

Being single for a long time can make you independent, selfish, stubborn and fixed in your way of life. It is good to have people with whom you can discuss your life decisions and whom you allow to advise you. Talk with your friends, your parents, your church leaders. You will also remain more marriageable!

● Sex and the single person

The expectation for Christian singles is that they will refrain from sexual relations with others. Sex outside marriage is not an option for a follower of Jesus.

This may be a very different viewpoint from that of the society you live in but it is God's standard and he will give you the ability to live a pure life. See Unit 13 on other aspects of sex.

● Friendships

Strong one-to-one friendships can be helpful but they can become very intense. It is helpful to have several close friends with whom you can enjoy spending time. Your friends also need to know your "agenda" in the friendship otherwise their expectations may be different! Group friendships are safer and very enjoyable for single people.

● Single parents

Single parents of small children often have little adult conversation and can feel lonely, isolated and very hard worked. It is a challenge for churches to support people in this situation.

sex

Sexual activity is only appropriate between members of the opposite sex in the context of a covenant married relationship.

● Good sex

✳ Genesis 1:28

What is God's command? _____

This command was given to innocent human beings before they sinned by eating from the tree *(Genesis 3:1-24)*. God intended a pure sexual relationship between man and wife.

✳ Genesis 2:24   ✳ Matthew 19:4-6   ✳ 1 Corinthians 6:15-16

How is the union between a man and his wife described?

_____

✳ 1 Corinthians 7:2-5

Why should a married couple have regular sexual intercourse?

_____

As a husband or wife, to whom does your body belong?

☐ yourself ☐ your spouse ☐ both of you

His left arm is under my head and his right arm embraces me (Song of Songs 2:6).

✳ Proverbs 5:15-19

How long should a man and his wife expect to enjoy an active, intimate, physical, loving and tender relationship?

Heartsearch

For those who are married:

How would you describe your sexual relationship with your spouse?

☐ poor ☐ fair ☐ good ☐ very good

How is it changing? ☐ deteriorating ☐ steady ☐ improving

How do you think your spouse feels about your sexual relationship?

☐ satisfied ☐ dissatisfied other_____

49

● The Song of Songs

This is a beautiful love song describing the tender relationship between man and woman. The story is difficult to follow but there are a number of scenes expressing the passions of love. There are vivid descriptions of the human body (4:1-7, 5:10-16, 6:4-10, 7:1-9), intense expressions of love and desire (2:1-17, 4:8-5:1, 6:1-3, 7:10-8:7) and the longing for a loved one far away (3:1-3, 5:2-8). There is a refrain echoing the power of love and a warning not to arouse it until the appropriate time (2:7, 3:5, 8:4). This is an excellent love song to read on your honeymoon!

● Sex before marriage?

✳ **Exodus 22:16-17**   ✳ **Deuteronomy 22:13-21, 28-29**

What should a man do if he has sex with a woman?

_____

What was the penalty for not being a virgin at marriage?

_____

Note that a man was obliged to marry the woman because he had sex with her and destroyed her virginity, not because she was pregnant.

✳ **Hebrews 13:4**

How should the marriage bed be?

_____

Avoiding temptation

In cultures which accept sexual freedom and where there is ample opportunity for sexual activity outside of marriage, it can be difficult for Christians to stand firm. Here are some helpful guidelines to avoid temptation.

- Avoid any undressing.
- Avoid lying down together - avoid beds.
- Do not press your bodies together.
- Leave your door slightly open if you are in a room on your own.
- Be extra careful when you are in a house alone.
- Set your limits at less passionate moments.
- Do not touch or caress sexually sensitive areas even through clothes.

Do not touch!

God's perfect way is for men and women to refrain from sexual relationships until they are married. This is not changed by the society we live in.

How would you describe your own interest in sex?

☐ not interested   ☐ interested

☐ very interested   ☐ obsessed

Heartsearch

● Bad sex - immorality

Sex is a wonderful gift from God but unfortunately it is often misused and has become a major source of sin for human beings. It is a vulnerable area of life for us all. This explains why there are so many warnings about bad sexual behaviour in the Bible.

50

What sexual immorality is mentioned in these verses?

Lev 18:6-18 _____

Lev 18:19 _____

Lev 18:20, Ex 20:14, Deut 22:22 _____

Lev 18:22, Lev 20:13 _____

Lev 18:23, Lev 20:15-16 _____

Lev 19:29, Deut 23:17-18 _____

Deut 22:5 _____

Deut 22:23-29 _____

Prov 7:1-27 _____

Matt 5:27-28 _____

Rom 13:13, Gal 5:21, 1 Pet 4:3 _____

Eph 5:3-7 _____

Can you think of any other sexually immoral behaviour prevalent in today's society?

_____

✴ 1 Corinthians 6:18-20

What do you sin against when you are sexually immoral? _____

What is your body? _____

To whom do you belong? _____

What was the price paid for you? _____

✴ 1 Corinthians 6:9-11   ✴ Revelation 21:8, 22:15

What will happen to immoral people?

_____

✴ 1 Corinthians 5:9-13   ✴ Revelation 2:20-23

Which immoral people should Christians be wary of?

_____

✴ Colossians 3:5-6   ✴ 1 Thessalonians 4:3-7   ✴ John 8:1-11

The past - Have you indulged in immoral acts which you are ashamed of? Repent and receive God's forgiveness. He will forgive and cleanse (1 John 1:9).

The present - Are there attitudes, thinking or behaviour that you need to put right in your life at the moment?

The future - Are there long term changes which you wish to make in this area of life?

sex

extra thought and discussion

• Clothing and nakedness

After the creation of man and woman they were naked and not ashamed (Gen 2:25). In this state of innocence their thinking about sex would have been completely pure and untainted. After they sinned by eating from the tree of the knowledge of good and evil, they became ashamed of their nakedness and covered themselves with leaves (Gen 3:7-11). Presumably many possibilities of lust and sexual immorality came into their minds and sex became a rude subject for human beings (Matt 15:19, Rom 1:24-25). God made clothes from animal skins (Gen 3:21) and the rest of the Bible assumes that men and women will wear clothes (Gen 9:20-23). Nakedness is a symbol of poverty, weakness, shame or immorality.

• Clean and unclean

Some Old Testament laws say that certain activities can make a person "unclean". This does not mean "sinful", but in such a state you were excluded from worship and sometimes from the community for a while. Some of these laws have a good medical basis. The laws regarding childbirth (Lev 12:1-8), menstruation and discharges (Lev 15:16-33) may seem rather odd, but remember that the Israelites of the time lived among pagan people whose religion involved fertility rites and immoral acts. The laws of the Israelites effectively separated sexual function from the worship of God. Apart from this principle which stands, there is no reason for a Christian to apply these laws (Acts 15:1-21).

• Love or lust

In good sex, intimacy and intercourse are ways of expressing love for the other person - they come first. In bad sex and lust, the emphasis is on getting the maximum pleasure for yourself.

• Oral and anal sex etc

There are no comments in the Bible about these and other sexual behaviour which may not be considered as straight sex. It is for Christians to assess motives and suitability of their sexual behaviour. It may be considered as unnatural (Rom 1:24).

• Prostitution and adultery

There is a lot in the Bible about prostitution and adultery because it is used as a picture of people turning away from the true God to worship other gods (Jer 3:1-3, Ezek 23:1-49, Hos 1:1-4:19, Rev 17:1-18).

• Solitary sex and masturbation

Masturbation is the manual stimulation of sex organs. Surveys show that solitary sex is widespread among both men and women in the western world. People use clothes, mirrors, pornography and other props. It can become a habit which is very hard to break even after marriage.

Comments

- There is no direct teaching about this behaviour in the Bible. By Old Testament law a man could be made "unclean" (Lev 15:16-18) which suggests that the practice would be discouraged.
- Christians who indulge in solitary sex can feel guilty and undermined in their confidence and witness.
- Self-control is part of the fruit of the Holy Spirit (Gal 5:23). We should be suspicious of any uncontrollable habit.
- It can be a self-centred and lonely habit.
- Solitary sex can be linked with fantasy and immoral thinking. Jesus said that this was also sinful (Matt 5:27-28).

Action

- Many find it helpful to talk over their behaviour with a mature, sympathetic person. This takes the loneliness out of the problem.
- Know when you are most vulnerable and take steps to avoid situations of high temptation.
- Know the grace of God and his forgiveness.

• Homosexuality

Sexual relations between people of the same sex are forbidden by God (Lev 18:22). In the Old Testament there is the death penalty (Lev 20:13) and in the New Testament exclusion from the Kingdom of God (1 Cor 6:9-10). The correct setting for sex is the covenant married relationship between a husband and wife. Homosexual behaviour is considered to be unnatural, lustful and perverted (Rom 1:26-27). It is a symptom of godlessness and false religion (Gen 19:4-5, Judg 19:22, 1 Kings 14:24, Rom 1:24-27, Jude 7).

• Acceptance and forgiveness

Temptation comes to people in different ways. Some people are attracted erotically to others of the same sex, children, animals etc. It is not a sin to be tempted but it becomes sin when we allow our thoughts and imaginations to become lust or if we actually engage in immoral sexual activity. Jesus had great compassion for people who were ensnared in sin but he never excused it - he came to set the captive free (Luke 7:36-50). As Christians we need be sympathetic and caring to people who are tempted in these areas and to help where possible. It is, however, not compatible to be a Christian and to continue in immorality (1 Cor 5:1-12).

• Bible examples

Rape - Gen 34:1-3, Judg 19:1-30, 2 Sam 13:1-20

Adultery and repentance - 2 Sam 11:1-12:23, Ps 51:1-19

Redemption of a prostitute - Josh 2:1-24, 6:22-25, Matt 1:5, Heb 11:31

marriage

● Marriage instituted by God

✳ **Genesis 1:26-28**   ✳ **Genesis 2:18-25**

Why did God create a wife for Adam (2:18)?

_____

The essence of marriage is friendship and working together for God.

What do man and wife become when they are united?

_____

Marriage mathematics
1 + 1 = 1

✳ **Matthew 19:4-6**

Who joins a man and his wife together? _____

● Covenant of marriage

✳ **Proverbs 2:17**   Before whom is the covenant made? _____

Marriage vows

There is no list of marriage vows in the Bible but there are clear principles showing what should be included in the promises. In some churches you may be able to compose your own vows. Here are parts of some often-used vows:

...will you love, comfort, protect and, forsaking all others, be faithful as long as you both shall live...?

...to have and to hold from this day forward; for better, for worse, for richer, for poorer, in sickness and in health, till death do us part...

...I give you a ring as a sign of our marriage. With my body I honour you, all that I am I give to you, and all that I have I share with you...

✳ **Malachi 2:13-16**

Which marriage promise is emphasised here?

_____

What two things does God hate?

_____

A covenant consists of a set of promises. There are four main strands to the promises made in Christian marriage.

Love - caring, protecting, honouring, respecting

Faithfulness - to have no affairs outside marriage

Sharing - of lives, bodies and possessions

Permanence - until death of one of the partners

Often the covenant is sealed with a sign such as the giving and receiving of rings.

✳ **Matthew 22:23-33**   ✳ **Romans 7:2-3**   ✳ **1 Corinthians 7:39**

When does your marriage covenant end? _____

Marriage is for this life. When your spouse dies, you are free to marry again. The only marriage in heaven is that of the Lamb *(Rev 19:6-9)!*

 Look at the marriage vows on the previous page.

If you are married - how well do you think you are keeping your vows?

If you are not married - consider how you would feel making these promises to another person.

● Responsibilities of a husband to his wife

What husband's responsibilities are mentioned in these passages?

Col 3:19 _____

1 Pet 3:7 _____

Deut 24:5 _____

Eccl 9:9 _____

Eph 5:23 _____

✳ Ephesians 5:25-33

This passage compares the relationship of a husband and wife to the relationship between Christ and the church.

How should a husband love his wife?

v 25 _____

v 26-27 _____

v 28 _____

v 29 _____

● Headship

✳ 1 Corinthians 11:3

God's way is for the husband to be the head of his wife. This does not mean that he should dominate her but he is the leader of the team and responsible before God for the conduct of the relationship. As with all Christian leadership it should be characterised by being a servant leader as taught and demonstrated by Jesus *(Matthew 20:25-28, John 13:1-17).*

● Responsibilities of a wife to her husband

What wife's responsibilities are mentioned in these passages?

Eph 5:22-24 _____

Titus 2:4-5 _____

1 Peter 3:1-6 _____

✳ Proverbs 31:10-31

Find some of the qualities of a good wife.

v 10 _____ v 11 _____

v 12 _____ v 13-19 _____

v 20 _____ v 25 _____

v 26 _____ v 30 _____

What do you think of these responsibilities? Which do you think are most important?

Heartsearch

As a husband or a wife how do you fare on these responsibilities and qualities?

Are there some which you need to work on?

Heartsearch

Ideal spouse?

What are you looking for in your ideal husband or wife? Tick **six** qualities which are most important to you.

- ☐ can cope with problems
- ☐ loves me
- ☐ will do what I want
- ☐ will tell me what to do
- ☐ loves having sex
- ☐ is stable and predictable
- ☐ is unpredictable
- ☐ is sexually compatible
- ☐ has a sense of humour
- ☐ is well-organised
- ☐ is popular
- ☐ is warm and friendly
- ☐ has good parents

- ☐ will make a good parent
- ☐ is a keen Christian
- ☐ is honest and upright
- ☐ is good-looking
- ☐ is dependable
- ☐ is intelligent
- ☐ is interesting to talk to
- ☐ has a nice shape
- ☐ talks a lot
- ☐ is a good listener
- ☐ is successful
- ☐ works hard
- ☐ respects me

✳ Exodus 34:15-16   ✳ Joshua 23:12-13   ✳ 2 Corinthians 6:14-16

Why did God command the Israelites not to marry from other nations?

It is unthinkable for a Christian for whom Jesus is their first-love to marry someone who does not share in their love for Jesus.

marriage

extra thought and discussion

• Marriage ceremonies

Various marriage customs can be traced through the Bible.

- Special clothing, jewellery, veil (Gen 24:65, Ps 45:13-14, Is 49:18, Is 61:10)
- Bridesmaids and attendants of groom (Judg 14:11, 20, Ps 45:14, Matt 25:1-10, John 3:29)
- Procession (Ps 45:14-15, Matt 25:1-13)
- Covenant (Prov 2:17, Ezek 16:8, Mal 2:14)
- Blessing by parent and friends (Gen 24:60, Ruth 4:11-12)
- Banquet and festivities (Gen 29:22, Judg 14:10-17, Matt 22:1-14, John 2:1-11)
- Wedding night (Gen 29:22-24, Joel 2:16)
- Gifts and dowry (Gen 34:12, 1 Kings 9:16)

• God's resources for marriage

Christians have many resources from God for the preservation of their marriage and for reconciliation.

- Love (1 Cor 13:4-7)
- Repentance and apology (Matt 5:23-24)
- Forgiveness (Matt 18:21-35, Eph 4:32)
- Prayer together (Matt 18:18-20)
- A covenant before God (Prov 2:17)
- Obedience to God (John 14:23-24)
- The Holy Spirit within (Rom 8:9)
- Sexual relationship (1 Cor 7:1-5)
- Headship of husband (Eph 5:22-33, 1 Cor 11:3)
- Church discipline (Matt 18:15-17, 1 Cor 5:1-6:8)

• Divorce - Bible principles

- Divorce was not instituted by God and was not intended by him. It was necessary to include laws regulating divorce because of our sin and hardness of heart (Deut 24:1-4, Mark 10:1-12, Gal 3:19). God hates divorce (Mal 2:16).
- God is a divorced person (Jer 3:6-10) and knows what it feels like to be rejected by an unfaithful partner. He can sympathise with us.

Case 1 - Husband and wife are Christians

- You should not even separate (1 Cor 7:10-11). It is God's command for a married couple to stay together (Gen 2:24, Matt 19:6). You should utilise all God's resources available to you to preserve your marriage (see above).
- If you do separate, you should remain unmarried and unattached and seek to be reconciled with your spouse. This should always be possible since it is God's will (1 Cor 7:11).
- If you remarry you commit adultery and cause the person you marry to commit adultery (Matt 5:32, Matt 19:9, Mark 10:10-12, Luke 16:18, Rom 7:2-3).

- Divorce is permitted if your spouse is guilty of 'marital unfaithfulness' (Matt 5:32, Matt 19:9). The word for 'marital unfaithfulness' is the general Greek word for sexual immorality (*porneia* from which we get our word pornography) and covers a number of activities (see Unit 13). If divorce is permitted then the covenant is ended and remarriage is allowed.
- However the whole tone of the Bible in this respect is forgiveness. When faithless Israel prostituted herself before other gods and abandoned the Lord, he was at great pains to woo her back again. The Lord's desire was for Israel to repent, for him to forgive and for the relationship to be restored (Jer 3:1-5, Jer 3:12-14, Is 54:4-8, Hos 2:14-16). All believers have been received back by God in this way when we were forgiven and we need to forgive others (Matt 6:12, Matt 18:21-35).
- Although you have the right to divorce your immoral spouse, the better way is repentance, forgiveness, reconciliation and restoration. Patience, love and grace are required.

Case 2 - Christian married to unbeliever

- As a Christian you may be married to an unbeliever because you unwisely married one, or you have become a Christian since marriage, or your spouse has lost faith in Jesus. Whatever the cause you should remain with your spouse and should seek to see them saved (1 Cor 7:12-16, 1 Pet 3:1).
- Your family is sanctified through you (1 Cor 7:14). This does not mean that they are saved but it does mean that your own walk with God and your service to God are not compromised by your marriage to an unbeliever.
- If your unbelieving spouse abandons the marriage, then you are not bound (1 Cor 7:15) - and are therefore presumably free to remarry.

• Remarriage

- Some people come into the church with a marriage history where it is too late to apply the above principles. Often one has to write off the past and start again.
- Young widows are encouraged to remarry (1 Tim 5:11-14). Similar reasons for re-marriage could be given to young divorcees (1 Cor 7:8-9).
- You are not permitted to return to an earlier spouse (Deut 24:1-4). This means that if your previous spouse has remarried, your covenant has been irreversibly cancelled and you are free to remarry someone else.

• Polygamy - many wives

It is clear that monogamy (one wife) was God's original purpose (Gen 2:24, Matt 19:4-6). Polygamy was introduced with Lamech (Gen 4:19) and several significant people in the Old Testament had more than one wife and concubines (others they slept with) eg Isaac, David, Solomon. It produced family strife. In the New Testament monogamy is assumed (1 Cor 7:2, 1 Tim 3:2).

family

The Bible's account of human beings begins with the family of Adam and Eve. Noah and his family are saved from the flood and the rest of the Old Testament is mainly concerned with the family of Abraham.

Abraham

Isaac   Ishmael

Esau   Jacob (=Israel)

Judah
:
David
:
Jesus

✶ Genesis 12:2-3   ✶ Genesis 13:14-17
Find *six* promises made to Abraham.

_____

_____

_____

_____

_____

_____

✶ Genesis 26:2-5   ✶ Genesis 28:10-15
Who else inherited the same blessings?

_____ and _____

✶ Galatians 3:16 Which descendant of Abraham spread his blessing to the rest of the world? _____

✶ Genesis 49:10 What was God's promise for the family of Judah?

_____

✶ 2 Samuel 7:8-16
Whose family in the clan of Judah fulfilled this promise? _____

✶ Matthew 1:1-17   ✶ Revelation 11:15
Who is the ultimate fulfilment of this promise? _____

Families are important to God and there is plenty of information in the Bible showing how people were related and the purposes of God for families.

Have you ever considered that God might have a purpose for your family?

Think!

● Families in the Bible

Families were extended and more similar to those we find today in eastern cultures. They included several generations, servants and others incorporated into the household.

Having children was seen as blessing from the Lord, particularly sons who were inheritors and who continued the family line *(Psalm 127:3-5)*.

● Father

The father is a central character in the family. He is responsible for the conduct of his family and the blessings of God upon it. It is his task to be a good example and to illustrate the fatherhood of God.

What are the responsibilities of a father?

Deut 8:5 _____	2 Chron 26:4 _____
Job 1:1-5 _____	Ps 78:1-8 _____
Ps 103:13 _____	Mark 5:23 _____
Matt 7:9-11 _____	Luke 15:20 _____
2 Cor 12:14 _____	Col 3:21 _____

● Mother

The mother shares the leadership of the family and many of the responsibilities above *(Proverbs 31:10-31)*. The Bible is full of examples of mothers showing tender sacrificial care for children. This is a vivid illustration of God's tender love for us *(Isaiah 49:15-16, Isaiah 66:13)*.

How did these mothers show their love for their children?

Ex 2:3 _____

1 Sam 2:19 _____

Matt 15:22 _____

John 19:25 _____

How did these parents go wrong?

Gen 25:28 _____	Gen 27:1-46 _____
Gen 37:3 _____	1 Sam 3:11-14 _____
1 Kings 22:52_____	2 Chron 22:3 _____
Jer 9:14 _____	

● Brothers and sisters

The word brother is used quite widely even for distant relatives. Love, loyalty and support are expected from brothers and sisters *(Proverbs 17:17, 18:24)*.

✱ Genesis 4:1-9   ✱ Genesis 37:3-11   ✱ 2 Chronicles 21:4

What are the main dangers in relationships between brothers or sisters?

Are you a father, a mother, a brother or a sister?

How well do you conduct yourself in your role?

Are there any changes you would like to make for the future?

● The family of God

The idea of family is used throughout the Bible.

• God is a family

God includes father and son and this family relationship is one of his eternal qualities (John 5:19-23, 14:9-13, 16:28, 17:5).

• As Christians we are children of God

We become children of God when we receive Jesus (John 1:12-13). God is our father (John 20:17, 1 John 3:1). We are adopted into his family (Ephesians 1:5). We are given the Spirit of sonship and can call God "Abba" (Romans 8:15-16). We are co-heirs with Christ (Romans 8:17). Male and female, Jew and Gentile, all receive full rights as sons of God (Galatians 3:26-4:7). We become brothers of Jesus (Matthew 12:49-50, Hebrews 2:10-12).

Some may find it difficult to accept God as father because they have had bad experience of their natural father. This is why we need the Holy Spirit which is the Spirit of sonship to enable us to relate to God as our father.

• The church is the family of God

Christians address each other as brothers (Acts 1:16, Romans 1:13). Family values of love, loyalty, friendship and support are expected among believers (John 13:34-35, Romans 12:10, James 2:14-17, 1 Thessalonians 4:9-10). Church leaders are called to care for their people as a parent cares for their family with love, care and discipline (Matthew 20:25-28, 1 Corinthians 4:14-17, 1 Thessalonians 2:7-12, 1 Timothy 3:4-5).

Heartsearch

How do you relate to God as your father?

☐ very good ☐ good ☐ poor ☐ very poor

How are you as a brother or sister in your church?

☐ very good ☐ good ☐ poor ☐ very poor

How do you relate to your church leaders?

☐ very good ☐ good ☐ poor ☐ very poor

59

● Your family

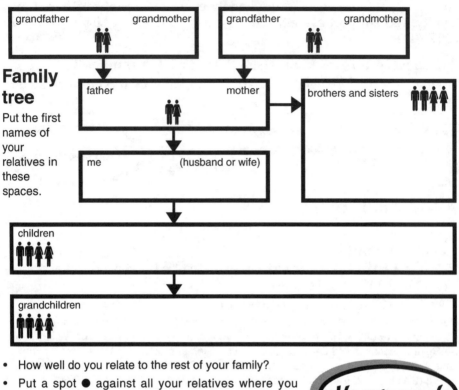

Family tree

Put the first names of your relatives in these spaces.

grandfather   grandmother

grandfather   grandmother

father   mother

brothers and sisters

me   (husband or wife)

children

grandchildren

- How well do you relate to the rest of your family?
- Put a spot ● against all your relatives where you know that God has touched their lives in some way. Can you see God's hand in your family?

Heartsearch

- Put a triangle ▲ against all the people who have or have had serious problems in their lives. Pray for those who are still alive.
- Are there any positive traits that you can trace through your family?

☐ health ☐ long life ☐ wealth ☐ happiness ☐ success ☐ kindness
☐ good reputation ☐ family stability   other _____

Thank God for the good things which have happened in your family.

- Are there any negative traits that you can trace through your family?

☐ illness ☐ poverty ☐ sadness ☐ failure ☐ crime ☐ immorality
☐ family strife ☐ divorce ☐ accidents   other _____

In the Bible there are families which are under the blessing of God and others which are under a curse for many generations (Ex 20:4-6, Ex 34:6-7). Pray that negative family traits will be destroyed and will not continue in your family line. You can be a starting point for the blessings of God in your family (Lev 26:40)!

health

● A good start — but soon spoilt

✻ **Genesis 1:31** What did God say about all he had made - including human beings?

_____

✻ **Genesis 3:1-24** Who tempted Adam and Eve? _____

Why did life become difficult for Adam and Eve? _____

✻ **Romans 8:19-22** What else went wrong? _____

● Why is there illness and disease?

The human race chose not to obey God, putting themselves outside his protection and making themselves vulnerable to the influence of the devil. Reasons for illness and disease include:

• **The universal fallen state of the earth and of human beings** — our bodies go wrong, decay and eventually die (Genesis 3:19).

• **The general activity of the devil in the world** — suffering is unevenly and unfairly distributed (Job 2:1-10, Luke 9:42, Luke 13:16, 1 Peter 5:8).

• **The sinfulness of individuals, nations or groups of people** — this is unlikely but sometimes needs to be taken into consideration (Numbers 12:1-16, Deuteronomy 28:20-29, 1 Corinthians 11:29-30).

● Is there a solution?

✻ **Exodus 15:26 – an Old Testament principle**
What are God's conditions for good health?

_____

✻ **Matt 8:16-17 – a New Testament principle**
How did Jesus carry our diseases (Isaiah 53:4-5)?

_____

✻ **1 John 3:8** Why did the Son of God come?

_____

✻ **Rev 21:1-4, 22:1-5 – the eternal cure**

● Jesus the healer

Healing people's bodies and minds was important to Jesus. He was often surrounded by crowds and healed every disease, disability and injury quickly and completely *(Matthew 4:23-25, 8:16-17, 9:35, 11:4-5, 12:15, 14:14, 14:35-36, 15:30, 19:2).*

✳ **Matthew 8:1-9:34, 12:9-23**   ✳ **Luke 14:1-4, 22:49-51**

Read these passages and write down the illnesses mentioned.

_____

_____

What questions did Jesus ask people before he healed them?

Mark 10:51 _____

John 5:6 _____

Matt 9:28 _____

Why do you think he asked these questions? Jesus was looking for faith — faith that he could heal and faith that he would heal *(Matthew 8:1-4).*

● How Jesus healed

Jesus did not pray for people, he usually spoke a *command* or *words of assurance.* What did he say?

Matt 8:3 — to a man with leprosy _____

Matt 9:29 — to two blind men _____

Matt 12:13 — to a man with a withered hand _____

Mark 5:34 — to a woman with bleeding _____

Mark 7:34 — to a deaf and dumb man _____

Luke 7:14 — to a dead man _____

Luke 13:12 — to a bent over woman _____

John 5:8 — to a paralysed man_____

Mark 9:25 — to a boy with an evil spirit _____

The work continues

Jesus's followers healed in a similar way.
- The twelve and the seventy-two (Luke 9:1-6, Luke 10:1-20)
- Peter (Acts 3:1-10, 5:12-16, 9:32-43)
- Philip (Acts 8:4-8)
- Paul (Acts 14:8-10, 16:16-18, 19:11-12, 20:7-12, 28:7-10, Rom 15:19)
- In the church (Acts 4:29-30, 1 Cor 12:1-31)

Jesus tailored his approach to the individual. If appropriate he linked healing with forgiveness of sins. He sometimes laid hands on people or touched the afflicted part of the body. Occasionally he did unusual things such as spitting on people's eyes or tongues or making mud and putting it on their eyes (Mark 7:33, Mark 8:23, John 9:6-7)!

- Jesus healed to prove he was the Son of God.
- He healed out of compassion for those suffering.
- He healed to encourage faith.

● Coping with illness

✳ **Psalm 38:1-22, 41:1-13, 107:17-22**   ✳ **Isaiah 38:1-22**

Consider how these people coped with their illnesses.

● What to do when you are ill

✳ **2 Chronicles 16:12**

How did King Asa go wrong?

_____

✳ **James 5:13-18**

What should you do if you are ill?

_____

What two things should the elders do?

_____

What kind of prayer is required?

_____

What else is required (v 16)? _____

✳ **1 Kings 18:41-46**

How did Elijah pray for rain? _____

What can we learn about the way we should pray for healing?

_____

● Motives for being healthy

✳ **Matthew 28:19-20**   ✳ **Romans 12:1**   ✳ **1 Corinthians 6:19-20**

What should be our motive for wanting good health? _____

63

Do you believe that God can heal people today?

Have you ever asked your elders to pray for you? Would you if you were ill?

Have you ever experienced being healed by God or do you know anyone who has been healed by God?

Think!

health

extra thought and discussion

• Preventative medicine in the Bible

The Old Testament has very wise advice about food and hygiene for people living in the Middle East at the time.

- Restrictions on eating meat and fish. Generally herbivores could be eaten but carnivores and other disease-carrying animals, fish and insects should not be eaten. Meat should be slaughtered and drained properly. Carcasses found should not be eaten (Lev 11:1-47, 17:10-16, Deut 14:1-21).
- No contact with dead animals (Lev 11:29-40).
- Diagnosis, washing, treatment and isolation of those with leprosy and other infectious diseases (Lev 13:1-46, 14:1-32, Num 5:1-4).
- Treatment of cloth and other items infected by mould and fungi (Lev 13:47-59, 14:33-57).
- Care with bodily discharges (Lev 15:1-33).
- Disposal of sewage (Deut 23:12-14).
- Contamination of water supplies and other objects (Lev 11:32-40, 17:15-16).
- Washing of hands and feet (Gen 18:4, 24:32, Ex 30:17-21, John 13:1-17).
- Cooking (Ex 12:9, 16:23).

• Doctors in the Bible

Doctors are mentioned in the Bible but they do not seem to be very successful because of lack of scientific knowledge at the time (2 Chron 16:12, Mark 5:25-29). A famous doctor in the Bible is Luke who wrote Luke's gospel and Acts and who probably attended to Paul (Col 4:14).

• Medicine in the Bible

The Bible is not written as a medical textbook but references to medical practices give us a good idea of methods used.

- Poultice for boils (2 Kings 20:7).
- Balm for soothing pain (Jer 8:22, 46:11, 51:8).
- Oil for wounds and skin toning (Is 1:6, Luke 10:34).
- Myrrh as an anaesthetic (Mark 15:23).
- Wine for wounds and for the stomach (Luke 10:34, 1 Tim 5:23).
- Eye salve (Rev 3:18).
- Splints and bandages (Ezek 30:21).

• Medical science vs healing by God

- If we believe that sickness is sent by God, it would be illogical to do anything to bring healing - any medical or spiritual means of healing would be thwarting the purposes of God! If, however, we believe that illness is basically evil then medical help serves to defeat this evil to some degree.
- Man's commission from God was to subdue the earth (Gen 1:26-28) and in medicine we bring nature under our control. We expect God's help with medical treatment supported by the prayers of Christians. There are tremendous opportunities for the Christian doctor, nurse etc.
- Unfortunately medical science is imperfect - drugs have side-effects, treatments sometimes fail and doctors can make mistakes.
- There is no need to feel guilty if we need to consult a doctor - it is not an admission of defeat! But it is important to pray as well!
- Diagnostic medicine may well help us to pray more intelligently and effectively.

• By all means?

Although it is good to defeat illness and disease there are some methods which we need to treat with caution.

- Remedies, practices, therapies or techniques which have their origins in other religious systems and which have a doubtful scientific basis.
- Spiritual healing which does not include the preaching of the Christian gospel of salvation. Supernatural power is not always from God.

• Mental health

Both mental illness and demonisation occur in the Bible (1 Sam 16:14-23, Dan 4:1-37).

- We should not assume that all mental illness is demonic.
- We should not ignore the spiritual dimension of mental illness and the possibility of demonisation.
- We need wisdom in knowing the right combination of medicine, counselling, prayer and deliverance.

• Christians who are ill!

We need not feel guilty about being ill!

Paul mentions several of his friends who were ill (Phil 2:25-27, 1 Tim 5:23, 2 Tim 4:20).

Paul himself was also ill (Gal 4:13-14) and the "thorn in the flesh" (2 Cor 12:7-10) may have been a recurrent illness.

trouble

✳ **Genesis 3:16-19** ✳ **Job 14:1**

What is the origin of our trouble?

_____

Trouble is universal to human beings and a significant part of our existence. Much of the Bible is devoted to trouble.

Tick the troubles which you have come across personally or which you have been close to.

Natural disasters	Violence	Health and death	Relationships
☐ earthquake	☐ war	☐ addictions	☐ death
☐ volcano	☐ civil unrest	☐ losing things	☐ bereavement
☐ floods	☐ crime	☐ arrest	☐ suicide
☐ drought	☐ robbery	☐ trial	**Relationships**
☐ famine	☐ injury	☐ disgrace	☐ loss of friends
☐ storms	☐ bullying	☐ shame	☐ arguments
☐ hurricanes	☐ harassment	**Health and death**	☐ disagreements
☐ pests	☐ threats	☐ illness	☐ family breakdown
☐ fire	☐ abuse	☐ disease	☐ divorce
☐ epidemics	☐ rape	☐ injury	☐ wrongly accused
Accidents	**Personal troubles**	☐ pain	☐ misunderstood
☐ travel accidents	☐ loneliness	☐ mental illness	Other:
☐ home accidents	☐ poverty	☐ depression	_____
☐ injury	☐ unemployment	☐ breakdown	_____
☐ fire	☐ drinking	☐ disability	

How would you rate your share of trouble in life?

☐ lots ☐ some ☐ not much ☐ hardly any

Heartsearch

What is the worst trouble you have experienced?

_____

What do you blame for your troubles?

☐ yourself ☐ other people ☐ society ☐ God ☐ the devil

☐ nature ☐ bad luck other _____

● Job's troubles

✳ **Job 1:1-2:10** What troubles did Job have?

_____

What was the origin of Job's troubles?

_____

What was Job's immediate reaction to his troubles?

_____

● Job's friends — a simple explanation

Three friends come to visit Job in his distress. They have a simple explanation for his troubles. What is it?

Eliphaz (4:7-9, 5:17-18) _____

Bildad (8:1-7, 20) _____

Zophar (11:13-17) _____

✳ **Proverbs 11:8, 11:17, 12:13, 12:21, 13:21, 13:25, 28:14**

What is the message of these proverbs?

_____

_____

✳ **Deuteronomy 28:1-68**

What is the message of this chapter?

_____

_____

What kinds of trouble are forecast for the wicked?

"Shalom"

Shalom is the Hebrew word for peace. It is a powerful word which includes completeness, soundness, prosperity, harmony, safety, health and absence of trouble. It also includes spiritual peace even when surrounded by the pressures of this life (Is 26:3). Shalom accompanies righteousness (Ps 85:10). There is no shalom for the wicked (Is 48:18-19, 48:22, 57:18-21)!

Peace is used throughout the Bible as a greeting, a farewell and a blessing (John 20:19, Eph 1:2). Jesus Christ is the Prince of Peace (Is 9:6, Luke 2:14, John 14:27).

The teaching of much of the Bible is that we get what we deserve. If we are wicked and disobey God then we bring trouble upon ourselves _(Psalm 7:14-16)_. We also put ourselves outside the protection of God and may be punished or disciplined by him through trouble.

Job's friends were using these arguments to convince him that he must be a sinner. There was a simple solution — he needed to repent.

Were they right or wrong (Job 42:7)? _____

Why?_____

Think!

66

● Job's reply — it's not that simple!

Job was not convinced by his friends' arguments *(Job 19:21-22)*!

✳ **Job 7:17-21**   ✳ **Job 9:2**   ✳ **Job 23:10-12**   ✳ **Job 31:1-40**

What point is Job making in these verses?

_____

Job does not think he is perfect but his suffering is quite out of proportion to his relatively righteous life. He challenges the justice of God. The fact is that many righteous people suffer and their suffering is not simply related to their behaviour (John 9:1-3).

✳ **Job 21:4-16**

What further point is Job making here?

_____   *Why?*

This is a common complaint (Psalm 10:2-13, 73:1-14, Jeremiah 12:1-2, Habakkuk 1:2-4,12-17, Malachi 3:14-15).

● God's reply — you will not always understand!

✳ **Job 38:1-42:6**

The book of Job finishes with a declaration of the power, wisdom and justice of God. What was Job's response to this revelation?

_____

● Reacting to trouble   How did these people react to trouble?

2 Chron 28:22 _____

Job 3:1-26, Jer 20:14-18 _____

1 Kings 19:1-5 _____

Job 10:1 _____

Ps 10:1, 22:1 _____

Ps 55:6-8 _____

Ps 88:1-18 _____

Ps 25:16-21 _____

Ps 42:1-2 _____

Ps 77:10-12 _____

Ps 18:1-50 _____

Lam 3:1-26 _____

How do you react to trouble?

Can you identify with any of the above?

Heartsearch

✳ **James 5:13** What should you do? _____

● A refuge in time of trouble

✳ **Psalm 9:9-10, 27:5, 32:6-7, 34:1-22, 41:1-3, 46:1-3, 71:19-21, 91:1-16, 94:12-13, 116:1-6, 138:7**

God is concerned about our trouble. As we turn to him in our distress he will help us to bear our burdens.

✳ **2 Corinthians 1:3-7**

What kind of God is he? _____

✳ **Isaiah 53:1-12**   ✳ **Matthew 27:46**   ✳ **Hebrews 5:7-9**

What did he do to identify with our sufferings and to carry them?

The suffering of God through Jesus is the ultimate answer to trouble.

What trouble do you have at the moment?

Bring it to the father of all comfort and to the son who suffered for you.

trouble

extra thought and discussion

• Suffering and persecution

In the New Testament, the idea of suffering mainly applies to suffering for the gospel. Jesus brought trouble upon himself because he faithfully spoke the truth, demonstrated the power of God, helped the needy and exposed evil and hypocrisy (Matt 16:21). For this he was nailed to a cross. All through history righteous people have suffered at the hands of the wicked - it began with Cain and Abel (Gen 4:1-8, Heb 11:4, 1 John 3:12-13, Matt 23:33-36).

As Christians we can expect to experience persecution as we stand for the gospel, righteousness and truth.

• Jesus promised that persecution was part of discipleship (Mark 13:9-13) - this is the meaning of "carrying your cross" (Luke 9:23-27).

• Persecution may come from the world around (John 15:18-21), from earthly governments (Matt 10:17-20, Acts 12:1-3), religious authorities (Acts 5:17-18), and even your own family (Matt 10:21-23).

• Paul suffered much physical hardship, trouble and persecution because he faithfully followed Jesus (2 Cor 1:8-11, 2 Cor 6:3-10, 2 Cor 11:23-28, 2 Tim 2:9, 2 Tim 3:10-12). However he experienced joy and triumph in his sufferings (Rom 5:3, Rom 8:31-39, 2 Cor 7:4), knowing the power of God and being privileged to share in the sufferings of Christ (Rom 8:17, Phil 3:10, Col 1:24). The sufferings in this world are only temporary, making way for eternal glory (2 Cor 4:16-18).

• We should pray and support those who are being persecuted (Eph 6:19-20). We are called to persevere in persecution (Heb 11:32-12:3) and God has promised to help and comfort us (Heb 13:6).

• The book of 1 Peter is good reading for those who are being persecuted.

• The end of the age

At the end of the age we can expect an increase in general trouble in the world and increased persecution of Christians (Matt 24:1-35, Rev 6:1-17:18). The Bible finishes with the return of Jesus, the destruction of evil and eternal trouble-free existence for the redeemed (Rev 18:1-22:5).

• Learning through trouble

Although trouble is generally a bad thing, it can be used for our benefit. We can learn patience, humility and love, becoming more sympathetic to others as we go through difficult times ourselves. We are encouraged to endure hardship as discipline from our loving father and to use everything that happens as a learning experience of life (Heb 12:4-13). Sometimes going through trouble will bring us to serve God in a new way - don't forget the vows you made when you were in trouble (Ps 66:13-14)! Times of testing can increase faith (James 1:2-4).

society

● The world

✳ **Galatians 3:22**   ✳ **Ephesians 6:12**   ✳ **1 John 5:19**   ✳ **Rev 12:9**

The word "world" is often used in the Bible for human beings and their activities here on earth. How is the world described in these verses?

_____

✳ **John 3:16-19**   What is God's attitude to the world?   _____

What did he do to show it?   _____

✳ **John 16:28**   Jesus came from _____ to _____

✳ **John 1:9-11, 15:18-19**

What is the world's response to Jesus and Christians?   _____

✳ **John 17:14-19**

Did Jesus want his followers to escape from the world?   _____

What did Jesus mean when he said his followers are _not of the world_?

_____

✳ **John 9:5**   ✳ **Matthew 5:14-16, 28:18-20**

What should God's people do in the world?   _____

_____

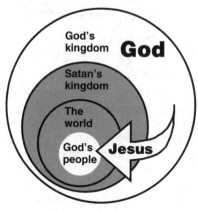

Jesus came into the world to bring the kingdom of God (Mark 1:15). It is the task of God's people to continue to work for the extension of the kingdom of God and to rescue our fellow human beings from the influences of the world and Satan. This will be achieved by our witness and conduct in the power of the Holy Spirit.

The rebellious activities of Satan and the world are permitted at the moment by God for reasons known to him. God is, however, ultimately in charge and can intervene at any time. All evil will be destroyed in the end (Rev 20:10, 14-15).

● Human governments

✱ Daniel 4:1-37

What was Nebuchadnezzar's sin?

_____

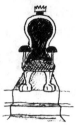

What did he need to acknowledge before his sanity was restored?

_____

_____

✱ 2 Chronicles 20:6   ✱ Psalm 22:28, 47:2, 103:19   ✱ John 19:10-11

Who is the ultimate ruler of the nations? _____

✱ Revelation 19:11-16   Who is King of Kings? _____

✱ Romans 13:1-7   ✱ 1 Peter 2:13-14

What should be our attitude to the governing authorities?

_____

Why should we obey them? _____

✱ Matthew 17:24-27, 22:15-22   What should we do? _____

✱ 1 Timothy 2:1-2   What else can we do? _____

✱ Jeremiah 29:7   ✱ Psalm 72:1-20   What can we pray for?

_____

How would you describe your attitude to your national and local government? You may tick more than one.

- ☐ obedient   ☐ supportive   ☐ encouraging
- ☐ prayerful   ☐ co-operative   ☐ complaining
- ☐ rebellious   ☐ disobedient   ☐ unco-operative

Heartsearch

Are there any changes you could make in your attitude?

● Active members of society

We are called to be law-abiding, good citizens of our country. Paul was a Roman citizen and took advantage of the fact (Acts 22:22-29, 25:11). Joseph, Daniel and Mordecai were godly men in high positions in secular government and as politicians were able to influence the nations they were serving (Genesis 41:41-49, Daniel 2:48-49, Esther 9:4, 10:1-3).

Are there ways which Christians can influence or serve their society and government?

● Dual citizenship

✳ Philippians 3:20-21

Where is our permanent citizenship?

_____

✳ 1 Peter 2:11-12

What are we in the world?

_____

✳ Hebrews 11:10-16, 13:14 ✳ Rev 21:2

What is the difference between our city here and the city of God?

_____

As Christians we may feel out of place and like foreigners in this world because we actually belong to another kingdom. We have temporary passports in this world - _we are in the world but not of the world._

● Standing out and standing firm

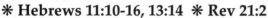

✳ Daniel 6:1-28

On what issue did Daniel find it necessary to disobey his earthly king?

_____

✳ Acts 4:1-22, 5:25-32, 5:40-42

On what issue did Peter and John find it necessary to disobey their rulers?

_____

Only in certain circumstances such as these can a Christian be justified in disobeying earthly authorities and obeying God rather than men.

✳ Psalm 82:3-4   ✳ Proverbs 31:8-9   ✳ Isaiah 1:17

On what other issues might we confront earthly authorities?

_____

✳ Amos 2:6-8, 4:1, 5:4-27

See how Amos boldly exposes sin, injustice and false religion. He stands firm for God's principles of righteousness and truth.

Heartsearch

Are you prepared to defend the poor and needy? Do you stand up for justice in your nation and in the world at large? Are there things you can do or say?

society

extra thought and discussion

• Going to court

Jesus strongly advised us to sort out matters before we get to court (Matt 5:25-26).

Paul explains that it is absurd for Christians to take each other to court and be tried by unbelievers (1 Cor 6:1-6). Conflicts should be settled in the church. Jesus lays down a simple procedure for settling a dispute (Matt 18:15-17) — first try to settle it between the two of you, if that fails take some witnesses along and try again, and if that fails take the matter to the church.

• What type of government?

In the world there are monarchies, republics, democracies, dictatorships, communists, socialists, capitalists etc. God is able to use various systems of government, such as the prophetic leadership of Moses or Samuel, as well as the more ordered monarchies of David and other kings. It seems that the particular system is less important than whether the leaders seek the will of God.

Some Christians are socialist, concerned for the welfare of those who are disadvantaged and the sharing of resources, while others favour the right wing, being concerned about individual responsibility and order. Whatever our view it is important as Christians to take our voting responsibility seriously.

• War or peace

War was a common feature in the Old Testament as nations defended or claimed land. God used armies for his judgments on nations, eg the conquest of Canaan by Joshua (Gen 15:16, Lev 18:24-28, Deut 7:1-6, Josh 5:13-15). Heroism is not always approved of (1 Chron 28:2-3). In the New Testament the emphasis is on the spiritual battle and Christians are called to peace. The role of soldiers, however, is respected and not condemned (Matt 26:52, Luke 3:14, John 18:36, Acts 10:1-4, Rom 13:4).

• Capital punishment

Capital punishment for murder is one of the first justice laws in the Bible (Gen 9:5-6). The laws of Moses include the death sentence for blasphemy, false religion, dishonouring God, sexual immorality, dishonouring parents and murder. It is worth considering that these laws were made for nomadic people living in tents with no facility for imprisonment.

• A tale of two cities

Much of Bible history can be seen as the conflict between the city of the world, typified by Babylon, and the city of God, typified by Jerusalem.

Early Babylon — The first wicked city in the Bible is that of Cain (Gen 4:17) and the wickedness of the society surrounding this city was eventually judged in the flood. Babel (=Babylon), characterised by pride and false religion (Gen 10:8-10, 11:1-9) was judged by confusion of languages. Sodom and Gommorah are cities in the same mould (Gen 18:16-19:38). Babylon itself, on the River Euphrates, continued to develop into a large and civilised city.

Babylonian empire — In 612 BC Babylon became the capital of an empire which lasted for around 70 years. In October 539 BC Babylon fell to the Medes and Persians (Dan 5:1-31). Babylon was the archetype of worldly kingdoms and empires. Chapters 2 and 7-11 of Daniel have descriptions of more empires which can be identified as Medo-Persian, Greek, Roman, an end time anti-Christ kingdom and the final triumphant kingdom of God.

End-time Babylon — The book of Revelation describes a Babylon in the end-time which contains the evil elements of earlier Babylon types and an anti-Christ world leader. There are many prophecies in the Bible which describe the sins and destruction of Babylon (Is 13:1-14:32, 21:1-10, 43:14, 46:1-47:15, Jer 25:12, 50:1-51:64, Rev 14:8, 16:19, 17:1-18:24). It is characterised by:

- Pride, rebellion, self-sufficiency and godlessness.
- Political and military power oppressing the weak and the people of God.
- Desire for world domination.
- Economic power, wealth and trade.
- False religion, sorcery and astrology.
- Sin and immorality.

The city and empire of Babylon is a graphic description of the world system in which we live.

Jerusalem — The first mention is when the king of Salem (=Jerusalem) blesses Abraham and receives tithes from him (Gen 14:18-20). About 1000 BC Jerusalem (also called Zion) was established as the political and worship centre of the Israelites by King David (2 Sam 5:6-6:19), and a magnificent temple was built there by his son Solomon. The city remained in the hands of the Israelite tribe of Judah (from which we get the word *Jew*) for about 400 years until 587 BC when it was razed to the ground by the Babylonians. The Jews (including Ezekiel and Daniel) were taken into captivity in Babylon where they lived as exiles. After the fall of Babylon the Jews were allowed to return to their city (Ezra and Nehemiah), but they never became politically powerful again. A large temple was completed shortly before Jesus was born. Jerusalem was destroyed in 70 AD by the Romans. This physical Jerusalem has been a visual aid for the New Jerusalem.

New Jerusalem — The heavenly Jerusalem is the company of all God's people through the ages (Gal 4:25-26, Heb 12:22-24). They are the people of the kingdom of God. The Bible finishes with the destruction of Babylon and the triumphant appearance of the eternal, perfect new Jerusalem (Rev 21:1-22:5).

old age

● Long life

✲ Genesis 5:1-32

Who was the oldest man? _____ What age did he reach? ____

In the Bible, old age is regarded as a blessing and a reward. How can we achieve old age?

Ex 20:12	_____	Ex 23:25-26	_____
Deut 5:33	_____	1 Kings 3:14	_____
Ps 34:11-14	_____	Prov 3:1-2	_____
Prov 3:16	_____	Prov 10:27	_____

● The joy of old age

✲ Proverbs 17:6 What are a crown to the aged? _____

✲ Genesis 50:22-26

To what age did Joseph live? _____

How many generations did he see? __

✲ Job 42:16

Despite all his earlier problems, Job lived a long life. How many generations did he see? _____

✲ Psalm 128:6

Family is a great joy to older people. Within the church family this can be extended to many others.

Are you looking forward to being old? ☐ yes ☐ no

Why? _____

How well did/do you know your grandparents?

Are there people in your church or community whom you could adopt as grandchildren or as grandparents?

Heartsearch

● Opportunities of old age

✶ **Psalm 92:12-15**   What can the righteous do in old age?

_____

Old age can be a very productive part of your life.

✶ **Genesis 12:1-5, 16:16, 17:1-27, 21:1-7, 23:1-2, 25:1-11**

Abraham was quite old when God called him and he began to see the purposes of God in his life. You are never too old to start serving God in a new way!

How old was Sarah when Isaac was born?___

✶ **Genesis 12:4-5, 13:1-14:24, 18:16-19:29**

How was Lot related to Abraham?

_____

How was Abraham able to help Lot? _____

How old was Abraham when...?
____ he was called by God
____ Ishmael was born
____ Isaac was born
____ Sarah died
____ he died

In old age we may have resources and influence that enable us to help younger members of our family.

✶ **Exodus 7:7**   ✶ **Deuteronomy 34:7**

Between what ages did Moses lead the Israelites?

_____

What physical condition was he in when he died?

_____

Why do you think God had to wait so long before Moses was ready to lead the people?

_____

✶ **Job 12:12**   What is a characteristic of old age? _____

✶ **Psalm 71:17-18**   How can we use this?

_____

✶ **Proverbs 20:29**

How can different generations help each other?

As a younger person, do you seek wisdom from older people? As an older person, do you have opportunity to help and advise younger people?

Think!

● Experience of old age

Ecclesiastes 1:12-3:14 Old age is a time for reflection!
What facets of life has this old man experienced?

1:12-18 _____	2:1-3 _____	2:4-6 _____
2:7-11 _____	2:12-16_____	2:17-23_____

What were his conclusions? _____

What does endure (3:14)? _____

● Difficulties of old age

Ecclesiastes 12:1-7

This is a cryptic poem describing some of the
problems of old age. Can you work out what is
being referred to?

v 1 _____

v 2 _____

v 3 _____

_____

_____

v 4 _____

v 5 _____

v 6 _____

As our bodies age, they become weak, perform less well and we may
develop various health problems.

✳ Genesis 27:1, 48:10   ✳ 2 Samuel 19:31-35   ✳ 1 Kings 1:1

What common ailments of the elderly are mentioned?

_____

Other problems of the elderly include *bereavement* as relatives, friends
and contemporaries die. This can lead to *loneliness* and *isolation*. Various
ailments may make it difficult to *communicate* and *move around*.

Heartsearch

As an older person do you experience difficulties and
problems in these areas?

☐ health   ☐ loneliness   ☐ mobility

As a younger person are there things you can do to
help older people with these problems?

● Responsibilities of old age

✳ **Psalm 90:10** What is our expected span of life? _____

Old age is a time to make arrangements for our departure. It is a time to pass on responsibility to the next generation. What did these people do?

Abraham (Gen 24:1-4) _____

Isaac (Gen 27:1-4) _____

Jacob (Gen 49:1-27) _____

Jacob (Gen 49:29-33) _____

Moses (Deut 31:1-8) _____

Moses (Deut 31:9, 24-25) _____

Moses (Deut 31:19, 32:1-43) _____

Moses (Deut 33:1-29) _____

Joshua (Josh 24:1-27) _____

David (1 Kings 2:1-4) _____

Paul (2 Tim 4:1-8) _____

Are there important things which you would like to do or say before you die?

Have you written a will? When do you intend to do so?

Are there things which your parents or grandparents said to you before they died? What has been the outcome?

Heartsearch

✳ **Hebrews 9:27** What else do we need to prepare for? _____

We need to ensure that we have faith in Jesus as our saviour. Those who believe in him will not perish but have eternal life *(John 3:16)*.

✳ **Titus 2:2** What other responsibilities do we have?

_____

_____

---

old age

extra thought and discussion

• Working life and retirement

In the Bible, twenty was the age of adulthood when men could fight in the army and had community responsibility (Num 1:3, 14:29, 26:2-4, 32:11). Old age was reckoned to begin at sixty and this was probably a common retiring age (Lev 27:1-8). Some of the Levite jobs required an age of thirty and partial retirement was at fifty (Num 4:3, 8:24-26 but also 1 Chron 23:24-27, 2 Chron 31:17).

• Respect and care for the aged

We are commanded to respect and honour the aged (Lev 19:32, 1 Tim 5:1-2, 1 Pet 5:5). Particular instructions are given to care for widows and the early church had special arrangements for their care (Deut 24:17-22, Acts 6:1-7, 1 Tim 5:3-16, James 1:27).

death

● The origin of death

✳ **Genesis 2:17, 3:19** ✳ **Romans 5:12**

What is the origin of death?

_____

✳ **Romans 6:23** What is death? _____

✳ **1 Corinthians 15:56** What is the sting of death? _____

✳ **Ephesians 2:1** What kind of death is being referred to here?

_____

There is a strong connection in the Bible between sin and death. As well as dying physically, we can be dead spiritually — this means that we are separated from God by our sin.

● Death destroyed

✳ **2 Timothy 1:10** Who has destroyed death? _____

What do we have now instead of death? _____

Jesus has conquered sin and death!

What has Jesus done?

Heb 2:9 _____

Heb 2:14 _____

Heb 2:15 _____

Heb 9:26 _____

This is the central message of the Bible. Jesus Christ came to take away sin. In doing so he removed the sting of death, disarmed Satan and opened the way to eternal life for all who believe. We are reconciled to God, no longer spiritually dead and have assurance of life beyond the grave with a new body.

● Biological death of believers

✳ **Psalm 102:11**   ✳ **Psalm 103:14-16**   ✳ **Job 14:1-2**

What is our life like? _____

We share in the decay and death of the earth around us *(Eccl 3:19-21)*. Our bodies eventually deteriorate, die and return to the dust.

✳ **Job 14:5** What has God determined? _____

Choose one or more of these words to describe your feelings towards your death. Try to explain your feelings.

☐ fear ☐ expectancy ☐ dread ☐ sadness

☐ uncertainty ☐ confidence ☐ joy ☐ relief

Are you prepared to die today? ☐ yes ☐ no

How would you prefer to die? ☐ suddenly ☐ slowly ☐ asleep ☐ active

Heartsearch

✳ **2 Corinthians 5:1-10** ✳ **Philippians 1:20-24** ✳ **2 Tim 4:6-8**

What were Paul's feelings about his own death? _____

_____

Death is a gateway to the next stage of our eternal life.

Mourning and burial

Mourning — The Bible includes many examples of mourning. People weep, wail, groan, lament, tear clothes, wear sackcloth, fast, shave their heads, play sad music, sing a dirge, take off turban and sandals, cover the lower part of the face and wear no cosmetics (Gen 37:34, 2 Sam 1:11-27, 14:2, Ezek 24:15-24, Matt 9:23, 11:17, Luke 8:52, John 11:31-37, Acts 8:2, 9:39). Mourning took place for a week or for one or two months (Gen 50:1-11, Num 20:29, Deut 21:13, 34:8).

Christians are encouraged not to grieve like others (1

Thess 4:13). There is special comfort for those who mourn (Matt 5:4).

Burial — Close relatives walked behind the body to the burial (2 Sam 3:31-35, Luke 7:12-15). The body may have been wrapped in cloth with spices and buried in a family tomb (Gen 23:1-20, 25:9-10, 49:29-50:14, 2 Chron 35:24, John 11:38-44, 19:38-42), at home (1 Sam 25:1), near a landmark (Gen 35:8), under a monument (Gen 35:19-20) or in a common grave (2 Kings 23:6, Jer 26:23).

Cremation — Cremation was only practiced in special circumstances when immediate burial was impossible (1 Sam 31:11-13, 2 Sam 21:12-14).

✳ **Genesis 5:24** ✳ **Hebrews 11:5** ✳ **2 Kings 2:11-12**

What was unusual about Enoch and Elijah? _____

For believers, physical death is no longer a punishment for sin and therefore not a spiritual necessity. It is usually a biological necessity unless God decides to take us in a different way, as in these two cases.

✳ **1 Thessalonians 4:13-18**

When will many others be taken without seeing death?

_____

● Rest in peace

✻ **Ecclesiastes 12:7**

What happens at death?

_____

_____

✻ **Acts 13:36**   ✻ **1 Corinthians 15:6**   ✻ **1 Thessalonians 4:13**

How is death sometimes described? _____

✻ **Luke 23:43** Whom are we with after we die? _____

After death it seems that we rest in the presence of the Lord, conscious of his love and waiting for the resurrection *(Romans 8:38-39)*.

● We shall rise

✻ **John 6:40, 44, 54** What will Jesus do for believers?

_____

What will happen (Matt 24:30-44, 1 Cor 15:51-53, 1 Thess 4:13-18, 2 Thess 2:1)?

- Jesus will come from heaven with a loud command, the voice of the archangel and the trumpet call of God.
- Believers who have died will be raised from the dead.
- Believers who are alive will be transformed and given new resurrection bodies.
- All will be taken to be with the Lord for ever.

✻ **Matthew 22:30**   ✻ **1 Corinthians 15:35-54** ✻ **Philippians 3:21**

Write down all you can about your resurrection body.

_____

_____

● Unbelievers

✻ **Daniel 12:2-3**   ✻ **John 5:24-30** Will they rise from the dead? _____

What is the difference between the believer and unbeliever?

_____

Our fate is sealed by our response to the gospel in this life *(John 3:16-18)*. Unbelievers also wait after death but away from the presence of the Lord *(Luke 16:19-31)*. Their resurrection is later than that of the believers and they immediately face God's judgment *(Revelation 20:13)*.

● Judgment

✱ **Romans 14:10-12**   ✱ **2 Corinthians 5:10**   ✱ **Hebrews 9:27**

Who will face judgment? _____

✱ **Matthew 25:31-33**   ✱ **John 5:19-30**   ✱ **Acts 10:42, 17:31**

Who will be our judge? _____

Because our salvation depends on whether or not we have believed in Jesus, he is in a position to determine our standing before the father.

✱ **Daniel 7:9-10**   ✱ **Revelation 20:11-12**   ✱ **Jeremiah 32:19**

What is written in the books? _____

If we expect to depend upon our good works to be saved, we will be very disappointed. Nobody has been good enough to earn their own salvation *(Romans 3:10-20).*

Book of life

✱ **Exodus 32:32-33**

(See also Ps 69:28, Dan 12:1, Phil 4:3, Luke 10:20, Heb 12:23, Rev 3:5, 13:8, 17:8, 20:12, 20:15, 21:27.)

Why is the book of life the most important book?

_____

How do you get your name in it? _____

✱ **Revelation 20:13-15, 21:8**   What is the second death?

_____

✱ **Revelation 21:1-22:5**   What is the final destination of believers?

_____

---

death

extra thought and discussion

• **Old Testament perspective**

The Hebrew word *Sheol* (NIV "grave") described a shadowy existence of darkness, silence and weakness after death (Job 10:20-22, Ps 30:9, 88:10-12, 89:48, 115:17, Prov 15:24, Is 14:9-11). Occasionally there are optimistic statements describing release from *Sheol* and resurrection from the dead (Job 19:25-26, Ps 16:10-11, 23:4-6, 49:15,

73:24, Prov 14:32, Is 26:19, Dan 12:2, 12:13).

Jesus proclaimed the resurrection of the dead by his teaching, his miracles and his own resurrection (Mark 12:18-27, John 11:17-44, 20:1-21:25)

• **Ghosts and spirits**

Any form of communication with the dead is strictly forbidden in the Bible. We should not consult mediums, attend seances or engage in any activity which seeks to contact dead people (Lev 19:31, 20:6, 20:27, Deut 18:11, 1 Sam 28:1-25, 1 Chron 10:13-14, Is 8:19). God himself may choose to demonstrate resurrection in special circumstances (Luke 9:30-31, Matt 27:51-53).